D1616237

INTRODUCTORY QUANTUM MECHANICS FOR THE SOLID STATE

Introductory Quantum Mechanics for the Solid State

RICHARD L. LONGINI

CARNEGIE-MELLON UNIVERSITY

PITTSBURGH

WILEY-INTERSCIENCE

a Division of John Wiley & Sons, Inc.

NEW YORK · LONDON · SYDNEY · TORONTO

TO MURIEL

AND THE BAR H.

PREFACE

This undergraduate text is designed to expound the basic ideas of quantum mechanics for atomic binding and for solids using as little mathematics as possible. The purpose of this approach is to help the student avoid the common confusion: where physics leaves off and mathematics begins. Partial differential equations, complex conjugates, and generalized orthogonal functions are introduced possibly for the first time in the student's work. There should be no difficulty in using quantum mechanics instead of fluid dynamics or electromagnetic theory to bring these mathematical concepts to the student. Some of the common physical examples, such as the harmonic oscillator, have been confined to problems. The physics of primary importance for our purposes is shown through examples of greater pertinence to the study of binding and of solids. Perhaps the greatest emphasis here is on linear aspects and how the physics follows with very few assumptions. The Fermi-Dirac distribution is derived on the basis of dynamics in order to convey the idea that equilibrium phenomena are the result of dynamic balances.

This work is meant to be of an introductory nature. The subjects that are taken up are carried only as far as is essential to establish a basis for further work. The problems are an integral part of the text.

The initial order in which the subjects are best studied is *not* the order in the book. It is recommended that, on first reading, the sections on the spherically symmetrical states of the hydrogen atom (beginning of Chapter V) be studied right after Chapter I. The subjects as arranged, however, are in the best order for later coherence. Such an initial change in order shows the student at an early stage that the seeming fantasy has real consequences.

I am grateful to several colleagues for the help in the development of this text and especially to Dr. Thomas Reichert for critical review of the manuscript.

RICHARD L. LONGINI

Pittsburgh, Pennsylvania
May 1970

CONTENTS

TABLE OF FUNDAMENTAL PHYSICAL CONSTANTS

Electron charge $\qquad q = 1.60 \times 10^{-19}$ Coulomb $= 1$ electron (e)

Electron rest mass $\qquad m = 9.11 \times 10^{-31}$ kg

Proton rest mass $\qquad 1836\,m = 1.67 \times 10^{-27}$ kg

Planck's constant $\qquad h = 6.62 \times 10^{-34}$ J $\cdot$ sec

$\qquad\qquad\qquad\qquad = 4.13 \times 10^{-15}$ eV $\cdot$ sec

(h bar) $= h/2\pi \qquad \hbar = 1.05 \times 10^{-34}$ J $\cdot$ sec or kg m^2/sec

$\qquad\qquad\qquad\qquad = 6.58 \times 10^{-16}$ eV $\cdot$ sec

Permittivity of free space $\qquad \epsilon_0 = 8.854 \times 10^{-12}$ F/m

Permeability of free space $\qquad \mu_0 = 1.257 \times 10^{-6}$ ($= 4\pi \times 10^{-7}$) H/m

Avogadro's number $\qquad N_0 = 6.02 \times 10^{26}$ molecules/(kg mole)

Boltzmann's constant $\qquad k = 1.38 \times 10^{-23}$ J/(Kelvin deg)

$\qquad\qquad\qquad\qquad = (11{,}600)^{-1}$ eV/(Kelvin deg)

Velocity of light $\qquad c = 2.998 \times 10^8$ m/sec

Some constants of	silicon	germanium
Atomic number	14	32
Atomic weight	28.06	72.60
Melting point	1693°K	1209°K
Relative dielectric constant ϵ/ϵ_0	12	16
Atoms per m^3 in solid	4.996×10^{28}	4.418×10^{28}
Crystal nearest neighbor distance	1.17 Å	1.22 Å
Energy gap at 300°K	1.12 eV	0.665 eV

INTRODUCTORY QUANTUM MECHANICS FOR THE SOLID STATE

I

QUANTUM MECHANICS BACKGROUND

In 1890 most physicists thought they understood all that could be understood. All that physicists had left to do was to more accurately measure physical quantities. Max Planck's introduction of quanta into thermal radiation theory (1900) was not taken as being of major significance physically until Albert Einstein showed the same quanta were involved in the photoelectric threshold (1905) and in the " anomalous" heat capacity of solids (1907). Following this period a great excitement grew and many patchwork theories were developed. Major contributions during this period by Niels Bohr and Louis de Broglie are well known. It was found that electrons behaved in ways that physicists had previously associated only with waves. By this time physicists were thoroughly familiar with electromagnetic theory—in fact most results needed for radar during World War II were available in 1895. The stage was set.

Under Bohr's guidance or prodding, physicists further developed the ideas of Werner Heisenberg (1925), Erwin Schrödinger (1926), and others almost as soon as they were produced. By 1930 hundreds of scientists had participated in this work. All the patchwork theories previously proposed had excited interest; previous work in electromagnetic theory had sharpened the tools. The surge of progress between 1926 and 1930 was the result of the pervading spirit of creation.

Perhaps one reason for the ease of comprehension and the large number of contributors to the field is that the type of equations and some of the philosophy involved were *somewhat* like those used in ordinary electromagnetic radiation problems. We are familiar with the wave nature of radio broadcast. Shorter wavelength brings us through microwaves, infrared, and visible radiation with no change in fundamentals. With light, however, we find a need for quanta, or packets of energy, and one early interpretation which joined the wave and particle or packet concepts of light considered the electric and magnetic fields involved in the radiation as giving us only the *probability* of a quanta being in a certain region. In fact, E^2 or H^2 were thus involved, and E and H, because of the form of their involvement, are known as probability "amplitudes."

A function in quantum mechanics which is a probability amplitude is treated similarly. Its rules are slightly different, and, unlike the E and H of electromagnetics, this function in wave mechanics is not in itself a measurable quantity. The rules for finding the function and methods of utilizing it for anticipating the results of physical measurement are the subject here.

MATHEMATICAL CONCEPTS

We assume here that the student is familiar with certain mathematical concepts needed to understand the work. A review of some specific and much used points follows.

Partial Derivatives

Partial derivatives are derivatives taken as though only one independent variable were involved, even though, in fact, several are. If ω is a function of x, of y, and of z, the "partial with respect to x" of ω is symbolized as

$$\frac{\partial \omega}{\partial x}$$

There are also partials with respect to y and z. The partial with respect to x is taken as though y and z were constants. Let

$$\omega = x\,e^y \sin z$$

Then

$$\frac{\partial \omega}{\partial x} = e^y \sin z = \frac{\omega}{x},$$

$$\frac{\partial \omega}{\partial y} = xe^y \sin z = \omega,$$

and

$$\frac{\partial \omega}{\partial z} = xe^y \cos z = \omega \operatorname{ctn} z$$

Complex Conjugates

A complex number involves the square root of minus one. However, there are always two square roots. Let these two be i and j:

$$i^2 = j^2 = -1$$

It is clear that for these to be different, $i = -j$ and $j = -i$. Then $ij = 1$.

These two roots are on a par with one another in that there is no physical meaning to the question, "Which is the positive root? Is i the fundamental root and j just its negative?" Thus any system of physical equations that involves i could have used j with identical meaning. In wave mechanics such equations are used throughout. *Every* time i is used, there could also be a *complex conjugate* where j (or $-i$) was substituted for i. This concept is important in much that follows.

Any complex quantity times its complex conjugate yields a *positive real* number and equals the square of the magnitude of the quantity. For example, the exponential

$$e^{i\phi} = \cos \phi + i \sin \phi$$

has a real component that goes from -1 to $+1$ since it is an oscillatory function. Thus the magnitude squared is

$$e^{i\phi} \times e^{j\phi} = e^{+i\phi} \times e^{-i\phi} = e^0 = 1$$

This is easily checked since the magnitude is given by the square root of the sum of the squares of the real and imaginary magnitudes. Thus the magnitude is

$$\left| \sqrt{\cos^2 \phi + \sin^2 \phi} \right| = \left| \sqrt{1} \right| = 1$$

Also note that the trigonometric form times its complex conjugate,

$$(\cos \phi + i \sin \phi)\ (\cos \phi - i \sin \phi),\ \text{equals}\ (\cos^2 \phi + \sin^2 \phi) = 1.$$

The real portion of a complex number can be stated as

$$\operatorname{Re} Z = \tfrac{1}{2}(Z + Z^*)$$

The real part of Z is always equal to one-half the sum of Z and its complex conjugate, designated Z^*. Thus

$$\operatorname{Re} e^{i\phi} = \tfrac{1}{2}(\cos \phi + i \sin \phi + \cos \phi - i \sin \phi) = \cos \phi$$

In dealing with complex quantities, note that the maximum value of sin ϕ is unity *only* if ϕ is restricted to real values. If ϕ is complex, then the value of sin ϕ no longer has an upper limit.

Operators

Mathematical functions are statements of operating procedures by which, given a number, we can find another number. The function $x^2 + 3x$ is a a statement that we can take the given number, square it, and add the square to three times the number. Another mathematical operation is differentiation. Thus $(d/dy)(x)$ states that the variation of x due to a variation of y is to be determined. If we symbolize d/dy by D we can write this as Dx. The function $x^2 + 3x$ could have been written as $(x + 3)x$ and we could have considered that the operator $x + 3$ was acting on x. We could have symbolized multiplication by $x + 3$ by the symbol η and written $(x + 3)x$, then, as ηx. Operators obey certain algebraic rules: $D + \eta = \eta + D$ but $D\eta$ does not always equal ηD.

PROBLEMS

1. Find the partials of s with respect to y and to t of the function

$$s = y + \alpha t e^{vt/x} + \tfrac{1}{2}gt^2$$

with x, y, α, v, g, t all independent variables.

2. Repeat Problem 1, with s and x dependent variables. Obtain $\partial s/\partial t$ in terms of $\partial x/\partial t$. Then try a particular dependency, $x = gt^2$. Do the answers check each other?

3. Find the partials with respect to x, y, z, and t of

$$\phi = e^{i\omega t}\left(\sin \frac{\pi x}{\lambda}\right)\cos \pi(y - z)$$

4. Write the (Maclaurin) series expansions of e^x, sin x, and cos x and show that

$$e^{ix} = \cos x + i \sin x$$

Using the series expansions, show that

$$\frac{de^x}{dx} = e^x, \qquad \frac{d \sin x}{dx} = \cos x, \qquad \frac{d \cos x}{dx} = -\sin x$$

5. Give an expression for sin y in terms of e^{iy} and e^{-iy}.

6. Express sin iy, cos iy, sinh y, sinh iy, cosh y, and cosh iy in terms of e^{iy} and e^{-iy} or e^y and e^{-y}.

7. Take θ and ϕ given as real. What is the real part of $-ie^{i\theta}$? Solve for ϕ:

$$e^{i\phi} = i$$

8. What are the square roots of

$$\frac{\sqrt{2}}{2}(1+i)?$$

Hint: Express in terms of an exponential first.

9. The operator $\partial/\partial x$ acts on the function $x^2 + xy$. What is the number produced by the indicated operation when the values of x and y are 3 and 2, respectively?

10. Operators x^2, x, and d/dx act on $\ln x$. Remember that the double operation

$$\frac{d}{dy}\frac{d}{dy}\psi = \frac{d^2\psi}{dy^2} \neq \left(\frac{d\psi}{dy}\right)^2$$

What are the results? If these are symbolized as operators $\hat{\alpha}$, $\hat{\beta}$, and $\hat{\gamma}$, respectively, show that

(a) $\hat{\alpha} + \hat{\beta} = \hat{\beta} + \hat{\alpha}$

(b) $\hat{\alpha} + \hat{\beta} + \hat{\gamma} = \hat{\beta} + \hat{\gamma} + \hat{\alpha}$

(c) $\hat{\alpha}\hat{\beta} = \hat{\beta}\hat{\alpha}$

(d) $\hat{\beta}\hat{\gamma} = \hat{\gamma}\hat{\beta} - \hat{1}$

(e) $\hat{\gamma}\hat{\alpha} = 2\hat{\beta} + \hat{\alpha}\hat{\gamma}$

Here = means "equivalent to" as operators may not have magnitudes. Show that the above operator equivalents also hold if the operators are acting on x^3. Do the equivalents also hold if the operators act on x? Try to construct a situation where any of the first three equivalents do not hold.

11. Given

$$\frac{d^2\psi}{dx^2} + m\frac{d\psi}{dx} + n\psi = 0$$

Solve for the constant b, given the form $\psi = a \exp bx$. Note that b has two roots, denoted below by b_1 and b_2. Under what conditions will the solutions be oscillatory? Try as solutions of the equation both

$$\psi_{\mathrm{I}} = a_1 e^{b_1 x} + a_2 e^{b_2 x} + c \qquad \text{and} \qquad \psi_{\mathrm{II}} = a e^{b_1 x} e^{b_2 x}$$

where a_1, a_2, c, and a are constants. Is there any special value that c must have for ψ_{I} to be a solution?

12. Show that in linear, homogeneous equations, as in Problem 11, gW is also a solution if g is a constant and W is a solution. Show that if W and U are both solutions, $c_1 W + c_2 U$ is a solution where c_1 and c_2 are constants.

13. Given

(**a**)
$$\frac{\partial \psi}{\partial y} = n\psi$$

(**b**)
$$\frac{\partial \psi}{\partial x} = m\psi$$

Show that $\psi_a = Re^{ny}$ is a solution to (**a**) and $\psi_b = Se^{mx}$ is a solution to (**b**). Show that R must be a function of x and S of y for ψ_a and ψ_b to be simultaneously solutions to both differential equations. Show that $Re^{ny} + Se^{mx}$ is not a solution if R and S are constant.

14. What are the real parts of ψ in Problem 13 when m is pure imaginary and n is real and positive?

INTRODUCTION

In our study of materials we are generally interested in aggregates of atoms. A given material may all be of one element or several different elements may be involved. The atoms in solids and liquids may be in regular geometric order or they may be randomly arranged.

Whatever the aggregate is, however, the atoms will be held together somehow. *All* aggregates may be thought of as being bound together by their electronic structure. Somehow the electrons achieve a lower energy state if the atoms are aggregated instead of widely separated. That is, when atoms are separated or "freed" from one another their electronic energy is higher than when they are grouped together. Thus the breaking up of the aggregates cannot be spontaneous since at least some of the electrons would have too little energy for their "orbits" in the free atom. This energy difference holds the atoms together because, in order to separate the atoms, energy must be given to the electrons to satisfy their need in the separate atom situation. To achieve the lowest electronic energy atoms form regular structures. Thus the structure of crystals or chemical compounds is determined by this drive of the electrons to fall down the energy hill. Even in the liquid state the atoms have some order, though not as much as in the solid. The atoms, in other words, are not arranged completely at random in the liquid state. The most stable low temperature structures are those formed when the electrons are about as low on the energy scale as possible. To convert to other structures, which must have higher electronic energy, it is necessary to add the extra energy needed to the system. The electrons have higher energy in the liquid state than in the solid; in the vapor the electronic energy is still higher.

Many of the properties of materials, such as electrical conduction, thermal conduction, and magnetism are *direct* functions of the electronic system. The crystal structure itself is one of the electron-dependent properties. Therefore clearly we must have a somewhat sophisticated understanding of the electrons. It is helpful to note first three principal properties of electrons that are not consistent with classical views of a particle:

1. Electrons are diffracted by crystals just as x-rays are. The electron is therefore presumed to have some wavelike properties.

2. In an atom the electron is said to orbit about a positively charged nucleus. However, only *certain* orbits are allowed. We may justify this by saying that the electron has certain wave properties and that the orbit of the electron must have *a* phase. The "head" and "tail," for example, must match as it goes around.

3. The very act of measuring the energy, momentum, or other characteristic of an electron changes its state so that past behavior cannot be extrapolated. This limitation covers all "small particles." "Small particles" are defined, in fact, as those particles or aggregates so affected. In addition there are large particles or aggregates that are so little affected by the measurement procedure that extrapolation is still possible; these are in the so-called "classical" realm.

In order to "observe" an atom we must use some means of detection. We could use a unit of light with a wavelength of about 1 atom diameter. This "quantum" of light must bounce off the atom to give us an observation. The light quantum has momentum and therefore it upsets the atom by transferring momentum to it during the bouncing process. Suppose we imagine a situation in which we as individuals are atomic in size. For a teacher to see this class he would bounce light quanta off the students. In order to "see" the approximate position of the individual (no details at all) the wavelength would be about 1Å (Angstrom unit). These quanta of light would have about the momenta that we, at lifesize, would associate with baseballs moving at 60 miles per hour. This would be upsetting to us, the observed, in just the way ordinary observations are to atoms. It is clear that it would then be difficult to judge the future from the past observations and a second observation would yield different results.

The simple classical picture of the electron cannot help us understand why some solids form good conductors and others form insulators. Yet "normal" conductors may have 10^{-10} ohm-meters resistivity at low temperatures, whereas a good insulator may have 10^{20} ohm-meters resistivity. This resisivity range of 10^{30} is a remarkable spread for any physical property. The conductivity of materials is proportional to the electron concentration times their average mobility (the velocity the electrons achieve in an applied electric field of unit strength). The electron densities of various dense states differ at most by small factors and therefore the mobility must be the property having this tremendous range of values. It would be impossible to understand this and many other properties if the classical approach alone is used.

The philosophy of physical sciences—the method needed to find out about nature—may clarify the problem. We make measurements and we formulate theories with which to predict results. Knowing certain characteristics and limitations we can predict certain measurable quantities. To answer the question: "How fast is it falling?," you will probably ask many questions, including the following:

1. How fast is *what* falling?
2. What is causing it to fall?
3. Where did it start?
4. Where is the measurement to be made?

In other words, the problem has to be defined. We then apply an appropriate theory, decide whether we can predict the desired quantity, and finally determine what the value of the predictable quantity is.

A theory that predicts values that cannot be measured or a theory that predicts the wrong values is not a useful physical theory. Quantum mechanics meets all the requirements of a good, useful theory. It does not permit physical interpretation when no measurements can be made.

In quantum mechanics there exists a function determined by the physical situation. The function is frequently symbolized by the Greek letter psi. This function contains *all possible* information about the system, which, in a simple case, may be a single electron:

$$\Psi = \text{the state function}$$

Quantum mechanics gives rules for *finding* Ψ for different situations and also gives the rules for *extracting information* from it. Physical measurements involve certain operations on the electron. Likewise, to predict the result of measurements, certain mathematical operations are performed on Ψ in designated ways. In fact, for each measurement there is an operation. We differentiate Ψ with respect to *distance* to find *momentum* and with respect to *time* to find *energy*.

This operation has a certain resemblance to Al Capp's Shmoo (probably correctly spelled Ψ'hmoo). The Shmoo, as you know, is a highly edible little creature that tasted like ham if fried, like beef if broiled, and like chicken if boiled. In like manner different operations derive various flavors of information from Ψ.

The difference between the state functions for different situations must lie in the variations of the environment of the particles. The electric field's forces, or other kinds of forces on the particles, vary from one place to another. These differences can be expressed conveniently in terms of the potential energy. Gradients of the potential energy yield forces in the usual classical situation, so the potential energy clearly contains all the local environmental factors that could influence the state of a particle. The potential energy bears a unique position in quantum mechanics: it is the one characteristic that is involved in defining individual situations. Furthermore, the potential energy is calculated exactly as it is in classical mechanics—even to the assuming of point charges, etc. Thus the potential energy for an electron in the vicinity of a proton is given by the negative of the work done on the electron to remove it:

$$V = -\int_R^\infty \text{force} \cdot dr$$

The force in the equation is of the usual inverse square law form. It is directed in the positive direction of the radius vector:

$$\text{force} = +\frac{q^2}{4\pi\epsilon_0 r^2}$$

In this case it is seen that the potential energy is negative. This is due to the arbitrary but natural choice of zero potential energy when the electron and proton are infinitely far apart and no longer influence one another. Then

$$V = -\int_R^\infty \frac{q^2\,dr}{4\pi\epsilon_0 r^2} = +\frac{q^2}{4\pi\epsilon_0 r}\bigg]_R^\infty = -\frac{q^2}{4\pi\epsilon_0 R}$$

FORMAL QUANTUM MECHANICS

The quantum mechanics looks at the world in a way that is entirely different from the classical way of viewing it. The ordinary mechanics is a special case of quantum mechanics applicable to large bodies; it is not proper to use classical mechanics in the case of small particles such as electrons. We will, however, keep classical mechanics in mind as we go into quantum mechanics. One way to approach quantum mechanics is to treat it as a game having certain rules. It is not a difficult game. As the game proceeds, it is found that the "goal" matches the characteristics of nature.

Quantum mechanics is based on several postulates.* These are most easily introduced by example. Suppose we wish to measure the x-component of the momentum of an electron. Clearly, if we know nothing else about the electron, such as the circumstances of the measurement, we could not get much of an answer. Right now we assume only that the circumstances are proper for measuring the x-component of the momentum and that, when such a measurement is made, we will get a unique answer. (The electron may be one shot from an electron gun; at the time of the measurement it is falling freely, having been accelerated by means of an electric field.)

Postulate I. There exists a state function which contains all possible information about the system.

Postulate II. Corresponding to each dynamic variable (measurable quantity) there is an operator. This mathematical operator is to be used on the state function. The operator corresponding to the x-component of momentum is

$$\hat{p}_x = \frac{\hbar}{i} \frac{\partial}{\partial x} \tag{1-1}$$

The circumflex ($^\wedge$) or "hat" as used here stands for "operator," so $\hat{p}_x$ is called the p sub x operator or the x-component of momentum operator. The constant of proportionality, $\hbar$, is called "h bar." Note the imaginary i. Since the operator $\hat{p}_x$ must have the dimensions of momentum, $\hbar$ must have the dimensions of momentum times length. The operator acts on the state function and results in the simplest possible linear homogeneous equation, called the "eigenfunction" equation:

$$\frac{\hbar}{i} \frac{\partial}{\partial x} \Psi = p_x \Psi \tag{1-2}$$

That is, the operation on Ψ produces the function Ψ itself times a *real constant* p_x, which is the measured value. This is possible *only* if a sharp value

---

* A postulate is something assumed to be true. It is used as the basis of proof and cannot itself be proved. In geometry, the postulates are known as axioms. By using the postulates given here we can prove many things. If another appropriate set of postulates had been initially selected, we could have "proved" the postulates used here. Thus the postulates chosen for this text are not unique.

Of Special Importance to the Student: Other references may use other postulates and therefore proofs or demonstrations of certain properties are not necessarily valid in the context of this set of postulates. Of course the reciprocal is also the case.

of the measurement is possible. The state functions ψ that can satisfy this equation are called *eigenfunctions* (or characteristic functions) and the sharp value of the resultant constant is called the *eigenvalue*. A value is said to be *sharp* only if a single, unique value is measurable. It must not, for example, be an average of many possible "sharp" values. This may seem to be inapplicable to our physical world because of our inability to measure precisely or because of the apparent inability of the phenomena themselves to be constant. State functions exist even when no sharp value exists, but then they will not be eigenfunctions. State functions which are not eigenfunctions represent states for which sharp values cannot be measured. It should now be clear that most, if not all, state functions appropriate to real physical situations are not eigenfunctions. This is the subject of a most important later section, Unsharp Quantities and Probability.

To be an *eigenfunction* of momentum, the state function ψ must be of the form

$$\Psi = a e^{i p_x x / \hbar} \tag{1-3}$$

Only in this case does the x-component have a sharp value when measured. It can be seen that with this form for ψ we have a solution to equation (1-2):

$$\frac{\hbar}{i} \frac{\partial}{\partial x} \psi = \frac{\hbar}{i} a \frac{i}{\hbar} p_x e^{i p_x x / \hbar} = p_x \psi \tag{1-4}$$

Here a is independent of x. The process of finding such a form for ψ is known as "solving" the equation. The coefficient $\hbar/i$ equals $(-i\hbar)$. The form $\hbar/i$ is preferred because it clearly cancels the $i/\hbar$ which results from the differentiation operation.

In the case of energy (the *total* energy) the operator is

$$\hat{E} = -\frac{\hbar}{i} \frac{\partial}{\partial t}$$

Note that the dimensionality of the proportionality constant, energy times time, is the same as that for the momentum operator proportionality constant and furthermore the two have the same magnitude (but are opposite in sign). These equations are, in a way, the simplest of their class. If a sharp value of energy is measurable, ψ must be of a suitable form to satisfy the eigenfunction equation involving the energy operator

$$-\frac{\hbar}{i} \frac{\partial}{\partial t} \psi = E\psi \tag{1-5}$$

where E is a constant, the measured energy. Thus in this case we must have

$$\psi = b e^{-iEt/\hbar} \tag{1-6}$$

where b is independent of t. The proportionality constant $\hbar$ will be explicitly involved in the theoretical expressions for measurable quantities and therefore can be evaluated. From experiments we obtain

$$\hbar = 1.05 \times 10^{-34}(\text{kg} \cdot m/\text{sec}) \cdot m = 1.05 \times 10^{-34} \text{J} \cdot \text{sec}$$

Plank's constant, h, is related to h bar by $h = 2\pi\hbar$. The relationship between h and $\hbar$ is similar to that between ω, the angular velocity, and ν, the frequency. In fact, $h\nu = \hbar\omega$.

If both E and p_x are capable of simultaneous measurements, then (see Problem 13) we must have

$$\psi = ce^{(i/\hbar)(p_x x - Et)} \tag{1-7}$$

"Simultaneous" is specified because the measurement will disturb or alter the state, thus making sequential observation unpredictable. An examination shows that c must be independent of both x and t. Thus, if simultaneous measurements were possible, a in (1-3) must have been a function of t and b in (1-6) a function of x.

In addition to the operators for momentum and energy, an operator to find position in postulated. The position operator in a one-dimensional system, x, is simply x. Thus the eigenfunction equation $\hat{x}\psi = l\psi$, where l is the eigenvalue, becomes

$$x\psi = l\psi \tag{1-8}$$

and l is the exact position of the particle along the x-axis. No ordinary function can satisfy this equation for *one* value of the constant l and *every* value of the variable x. Yet this must be so for ψ to be an eigenfunction. Each eigenfunction must have its single, unique eigenvalue. It is clear that in order for this to have a solution, ψ must be zero for $x \neq l$ and finite or infinite for $x = l$. This gives us an idea that the magnitude of ψ is also related to position. The eigenfunctions for the position operator are called delta functions. For our purposes these functions can be defined by the relationships

$$\delta(a - a') = 0, \qquad a \neq a' \tag{1-9}$$

and, to use a form compatible with our other eigenfunctions,

$$\int |\delta(a - a')|^2 \, da = 1 \tag{1-10}$$

when integrated over all values of a. The delta function may be thought of as a limit of some analytic expression. No particular limit is preferred. It *may* have the form, in a one dimensional system, of

$$\delta(x - a) = \lim_{\alpha \to \infty} \alpha^{1/2} (2/\pi)^{1/4} e^{-\alpha^2(x-a)^2} \tag{1-11}$$

As α approaches its limit, the exponential causes a rapid drop off for $x \neq a$ even though the coefficient gets indefinitely large. It is clear that $\hat{x}\delta(x-a) = x\delta(x-a) = a\delta(x-a)$ and therefore δ is the required spatial eigenfunction. In most mathematical treatises the delta function has the form of the square of the function used here so that they do not have the character of eigenfunctions. In the cases where ψ is not a delta function we cannot state an exact position for the electron. We will show later (see Chapter III) that $|\psi|^2$ is proportional to the probability of finding a particle at a given location —or to the charge density if the particle is an electron.

The last postulated operator is that for potential energy. The operator $\hat{V} \rightarrow V$ just as $\hat{x} \rightarrow x$. Thus we have two operators defined by differentiation which have the same constant of proportionality (except for sign), $\hbar/i$, and two operators which are just the variables themselves. If V is a function of position such as gr^{-1}, then we substitute the algebraic quantity gr^{-1} for V.

The Hamiltonian

For a particle moving in the x direction in a field-free space the total energy is given, according to classical mechanics, by

$$E = V + E_{\text{kinetic}} = V + \tfrac{1}{2}mv^2 = V + \tfrac{1}{2}\frac{m^2v^2}{m}$$

$$= V + \frac{p^2}{2m} \tag{1-12}$$

We now make a third postulate which ties quantum mechanics to classical mechanics.

Postulate III. The operator for any other measurement (any for which the operator was not postulated) is found by expressing the quantities to be measured classically in terms of energy, momentum, potential, and position. Then the four previously postulated operators are substituted for the classical quantities.

In "operator language" the kinetic energy of (1-12) would be expressed as $\hat{p} \cdot \hat{p}/2m$, or

$$\frac{1}{2m}\left(\frac{\hbar}{i}\frac{\partial}{\partial x}\right)\left(\frac{\hbar}{i}\frac{\partial\psi}{\partial x}\right) = -\frac{\hbar^2}{2m}\frac{\partial^2\psi}{\partial x^2} \tag{1-13}$$

Thus (1-12) becomes

$$\left(-\frac{\hbar^2}{2m}\frac{\partial^2}{\partial x^2} + \hat{V}\right)\psi = E\psi \tag{1-14}$$

Note the parentheses around the two operators. The ψ does not "factor" out but the parentheses indicate that both operators act on ψ and that the result is summed according to sign.

We saw earlier

$$-\frac{\hbar}{i}\frac{\partial}{\partial t}\psi = E\psi \tag{1-5}$$

and therefore we must also have

$$\left(-\frac{\hbar^2}{2m}\frac{\partial^2}{\partial x^2} + V\right)\psi = -\frac{\hbar}{i}\frac{\partial}{\partial t}\psi \tag{1-15}$$

Thus we see that for energy there are two operators and equation (1-15) is merely a statement that they must yield the same result. In the case of three dimensions this new energy operator (called the Hamiltonian) is given by

$$\hat{H} \to \frac{1}{2m}(\hat{p}_x{}^2 + \hat{p}_y{}^2 + \hat{p}_z{}^2) + \hat{V}$$

When the mathematical operations are put in explicitly and V replaces $\hat{V}$, the Hamiltonian becomes

$$-\frac{\hbar^2}{2m}\left(\frac{\partial^2}{\partial x^2} + \frac{\partial^2}{\partial y^2} + \frac{\partial^2}{\partial z^2}\right)\psi + V\psi = -\frac{\hbar}{i}\frac{\partial}{\partial t}\psi \tag{1-16}$$

In vector notation the quantities in brackets are indicated simply by ∇^2, called del squared, and the equation becomes

$$-\frac{\hbar^2}{2m}\nabla^2\psi + V\psi = -\frac{\hbar}{i}\frac{\partial}{\partial t}\psi \tag{1-17}$$

The vector operator is simpler to write and makes conversion to non-rectangular coordinates clearer. Del squared in spherical coordinates, for example, is well known* and the symbol's use here indicates that the equation changes its form for various coordinate systems just as vectors do. Note that we have equated the energy E to the sum of a kinetic and potential term, as E is the total energy.

Stationary States

Our greatest interest here will be in the so-called *stationary states*. These states have state functions which are eigenfunctions of the energy operator;

* See discussion of Schrödinger equation in Chapter V.

thus they must always have solutions of the form

$$\Psi = \psi e^{-iEt/\hbar} \tag{1-18}$$

Here ψ is position dependent only and all the time dependence is cyclic and in the exponential. (*Stationary*, as used here, implies that time dependence and spatial dependence are separable.) The solution (1-18) can be checked by putting it into equation (1-16) or the vector equation (1-17):

$$-\frac{\hbar^2}{2m} e^{-iEt/\hbar} \nabla^2 \psi + e^{-iEt/\hbar} V\psi = Ee^{-iEt/\hbar}\psi \tag{1-19}$$

The ∇^2 operator (that is, the spatial derivative operator) does not operate on the explicit exponential since no spatial dependence is involved. Thus $\exp -i(Et/\hbar)$ is a common factor and divides out. We then obtain

$$-\frac{\hbar^2}{2m} \nabla^2 \psi + V\psi = E\psi \tag{1-20}$$

Note that ψ in (1-20) is independent of time and therefore "stationary." Equations (1-16), (1-17), and (1-20) are various forms of the Schrödinger (Schroedinger) equation.

The "operator"

$$\left[-\frac{\hbar^2}{2m} \nabla^2 + V \right]$$

is the "Hamiltonian" and is designated by $\hat{H}$. Thus (1-20) might have been written

$$\hat{H}\psi = E\psi \tag{1-21}$$

Here the functions ψ that satisfy the equation are the eigenfunctions, and the corresponding constants E are the eigenvalues. Note that the ψ of equations (1-19) and (1-20) is only the position-dependent portion of the state function Ψ. It *should not be construed* that the state function is independent of time. The time factor is simply not included in ψ. It should further be noted that the use of the symbols Ψ and ψ here is purely arbitrary and they are not used in this way consistently in the following discussion.

The Hamiltonian operator is the most important operator in quantum mechanics. It contains the potential energy V. The potential is the *only* connection between the quantum mechanical formulation and the "real world." The way a ball rolls downhill, the reason a pendulum swings, or the difficulty of leaving the earth can all be stated in terms of the potential energy being a function of position. In like manner electrons behave in ways determined by the spatial (meaning function of position in space) dependence of the potential energy (frequently just called "potential"). In this book we limit the discussion of potential energy to that resulting from Coulomb's Law. By proper formulation of the potential function and proper application of it in equation (1-17), it is possible (at least in principle) to determine the system state function, and through it, to determine the results of other measurements.

All state functions dealt with hereafter will be assumed to satisfy the time-dependent Schrödinger equation (1-17), the only tie to the "real" world. Thus, to describe real situations, we must first have some potential function. Electrons are confined to a small region of space if the potential increases rapidly going away from that region. Some simplified models of potential situations will be used extensively in the following chapters.

PROBLEMS

15. Derive the dimensions of $\hbar$ from each of the eigenfunction equations (1-2) and (1-5). Show in terms of length, time, and mass that these are indeed the same. Show also that $(kg \cdot m/sec) \cdot m$ and $J \cdot sec$ are identical units (dimensions and magnitude).

16. What momentum is associated with an electron whose eigenfunction is given by

$$\psi = g \exp \frac{-i2\pi x}{\lambda}$$

where λ is a constant?

ψ^* is the complex conjugate of ψ. Is the magnitude of $\psi\psi^*$ a function of position? Is $\psi\psi^*$ always real and positive?

17. All symbols have their usual meaning. Can these be eigenvalues? If not, what are the reasons? If so, of what can they be eigenvalues?

$$\frac{2\pi\hbar}{\lambda}$$

$$i$$

$$\sin \pi mk$$

$$\frac{p^2}{2m}$$

$$\hbar t^{-1}$$

18. Show whether or not it is possible to measure the momentum and get a unique answer when an electron is associated with the state function

$$\psi = ae^{iBt} \sin(2\pi x \lambda^{-1})$$

How does the value of $\psi\psi^*$ vary with position in this case? If $B = 0$, what would be the energy associated with ψ? Is this contradictory? Give a general expression for B.

19. The stationary portion of the state function is given as

$$\psi = b \cos \alpha x + c \sin \alpha x$$

Under what conditions is this an eigenfunction for $\hat{p}_x$?
What is the sharp value of momentum associated with the relationship you specified between b and c?

20. Is the state function of Problem 19 an eigenfunction of the Hamiltonian? Is this only true if all conditions are met for it also to be a momentum eigenfunction? What is the time-dependent factor that is missing from the expression?

21. Is the constant g a momentum eigenvalue of the state function $\psi = M \cos gx/\hbar$? Here M is independent of x.
If $g^2/2m$ is an energy eigenvalue, what value must the potential energy have? Is M a function of time? Give the time dependence explicitly.

22. A harmonic oscillator is one which finds that a displacement results in a restoring force proportional to the displacement. The potential function for such a system is $V = V_0 + gx^2$. State the form of the Hamiltonian operator explicitly.

23. The Z-component of angular momentum is given in classical mechanics as $M_z = xp_y - yp_x$. (From the vector relationship $\mathbf{m} = \mathbf{r} \times \mathbf{p}$.) What is the proper quantum mechanical operator? What is the eigenfunction equation?

24. Determine whether $\psi = A \cos p_x x/\hbar$ is a spatial (one-dimensional) eigenfunction of the energy operator when V is a constant. If so, what is the energy? Is ψ an eigenfunction of momentum? Determine whether ψ is an eigenfunction of energy if the potential energy V is given by $V = kx^2$.

25. Is ψ an energy eigenfunction? If so, what is the measurable energy value in terms of α and in terms of β? Here

$$\psi = e^{i\beta t}(A \sin \alpha x + Bi \cos \alpha x)$$

The potential energy is V_0.

II

PROBABILITY

LIMITS ON FUNCTIONS AND OPERATORS

In quantum mechanics there are certain required limitations and in the *usual* situation we cannot make precise measurements. In this chapter we examine this situation. First we must examine restrictions that are placed on functions and operators.

Function Restrictions

Certain seemingly obvious limitations are postulated on the nature of the allowable state functions. The state functions represent the state of actual physical situations.

Postulate IV. The state function ψ:
(a) Must be finite and continuous.
(b) Must be single valued.

(c)
$$\int \psi^* \psi \, d\tau = 1 \tag{2-1}$$

(d) This ψ must go to zero at infinity. The space available is finite—that is, the real world. This may be thought of as an explicit statement of one aspect of (c). (See Problems 1 and 2.)

Comments. Point (a) indicates that this finite limit on ψ excludes the delta function eigenfunctions of position. This means that sharp position values cannot be found in the real world. For mathematical reasons the postulate is frequently stated "except at a finite number of points." The state functions are limited by the postulate as given, and otherwise this postulate, with the exception stated, also refers to eigenfunctions. As we shall see in Chapter III, this postulate could have been deduced for the special case of energy eigenfunctions of real systems. The eigenfunctions are mathematical extremes of the state functions and, as such, may have certain characteristics not allowed the state functions appropriate to physically real situations.

Point (b) does not imply that the derivative of ψ cannot have a sudden jump in value.

Point (c) is known as the "normalizing" condition. The asterisk (*) denotes "the complex conjugate of . . ." and $d\tau$ is an element of volume ($= dx\, dy\, dz$ for a simple particle). As shown in the Mathematical Background section $\psi\psi^*$ is a *positive real* number equal to the square of the magnitude of ψ. The integration is over the complete range of available space. Throughout this book we used the symbols $\int \cdots d\tau$ to indicate integration over all space. Here $d\tau$ is an element of "volume," meaning *length* in a one-dimensional case, *area* in a two-dimensional case, or *conventional volume* in a three-dimensional case. In one-dimensional systems $d\tau = dx$. In two dimensions, then, $d\tau$ might be $dx\, dy$ in a rectangular system or $r d\theta\, dr$ in a circular system. No limits of integration will be shown specifically. The requirement that the integral be equal to *one* is clearly also a requirement that the integral be finite (and nonzero). Since ψ will be employed with operators only in linear, homogeneous equations where it is clear that any constant will factor out, the setting of the integral equal to unity merely defines the factorable constant. So-called normalization will be useful. In fact, normalization is imperative when $|\psi|^2$ (which equals $\psi\psi^*$) is interpreted as probability (or proportional to charge density) as suggested earlier. Then it is clear that the integral will simply be a statement that the sum of probabilities of all possible situations is unity. We will use ψ in this "normalized" form in most of what follows.

A corollary, sometimes stated as a postulate, defines the character of $\partial\psi/\partial x$ or $\nabla\psi$ where ψ is an energy eigenfunction. For a discussion see equations (3-8) to (3-11).

Although it is not stated in this postulate, recall that all state functions, to be related to the real world, must satisfy Schrödinger's equation.

Realness of Computed Measurable Quantities: Operator Restrictions

It was stated earlier that only *real* quantities are measurable and that quantum mechanics predicts only measurable quantities. Thus quantum mechanics must predict only real quantities. This will be *postulated*. But our postulates must be at least consistent within themselves and must be operational, so this postulate must put some limits on what can be done. It turns out to be limiting as far as the operators are concerned. The operators will be required to satisfy the *Hermitian condition*, as we shall see.

We wish all predicted values of measurable quantities to be real. How do we express this mathematically? For an operator $\hat{\alpha}$ we have the predicted measurable quantity α which, then, must be real. This means that the imaginary component of it, when plotted on a complex plane, is zero. Its complex conjugate, α^*, has the same real component and the opposite complex component, which, as previously stated, must be zero. Thus in the case of real α we have $\alpha = \alpha^*$. That is, our postulate says that any predicted measurable quantity α equals its complex conjugate.

Now let us examine the implications of this statement. We find α, according to our rules, by

$$\hat{\alpha}\psi = \alpha\psi \qquad (2\text{-}2)$$

The operator $\hat{\alpha}$ corresponds to some measurement, and α is its eigenvalue, the unique result of that measurement. The complex conjugate equation must also hold (see Mathematical Concepts section of Chapter I). In fact it means exactly the same thing physically. Thus

$$\hat{\alpha}^*\psi^* = \alpha^*\psi^* = \alpha\psi^* \qquad (2\text{-}3)$$

[As an example, the complex conjugate of the momentum operator $(\hbar/i)(\partial/\partial x)$ is $(-\hbar/i)(\partial/\partial x)$.] We just saw that we can substitute α for α^*. Now we multiply equation (2-2) by ψ^* and equation (2-3) by ψ. Since $\hat{\alpha}$ and $\hat{\alpha}^*$ are operators, and we want the multiplication to be just multiplication, we must place the new factors to the left of the operator symbols since, by convention, operators operate on those functions to their right. Thus, since α is a constant,

$$\psi^*(\hat{\alpha}\psi) = \psi^*(\alpha\psi) = \alpha\psi^*\psi \qquad (2\text{-}4)$$

and

$$\psi(\hat{\alpha}^*\psi^*) = \psi(\alpha^*\psi^*) = \alpha^*\psi\psi^* = \alpha\psi\psi^* \qquad (2\text{-}5)$$

One consequence of this is that for α to be real, apparently

$$\psi^*(\hat{\alpha}\psi) - \psi(\hat{\alpha}^*\psi^*) = 0 \qquad (2\text{-}6)$$

Although we do not demonstrate it here, this proves to be unnecessarily restrictive (see Problem 3). Since differential equations are involved, it is really necessary to integrate them before it is known whether or not an eigenfunction or its eigenvalue fit. A sufficient restriction, then, in order to insure the prediction of real quantities, is that this averages to zero when integrated over all space:

$$\int [\psi^*\hat{\alpha}\psi - \psi\hat{\alpha}^*\psi^*] \, d\tau = 0$$

or

$$\int \psi^*\hat{\alpha}\psi \, d\tau - \int \psi\hat{\alpha}^*\psi^* \, d\tau = 0$$

We generalize this, however, putting it in the form

$$\int \phi^*\hat{\alpha}\psi \, d\tau - \int \psi\hat{\alpha}^*\phi^* \, d\tau = 0 \tag{2-7}$$

where ϕ is any eigenfunction of $\hat{\alpha}$ (ϕ may be equal to ψ). This integral form is known as the *Hermitian condition*.

The generalization needed to reach this form has significant implications. This broadening of the scope will prove to be important in the section on Expansion Theorems and Orthogonality. In utilizing Postulate III ambiguities occasionally arise. The Hermitian condition then is used to determine the correct operator form. (See Problem 18 for a way out of the dilemma concerning the choice of functions to use for testing.)

Postulate V. Given any two eigenfunctions ψ and ϕ of the quantum mechanical operator $\hat{\alpha}$, the Hermitian condition,

$$\int \phi^*\hat{\alpha}\psi \, d\tau = \int \psi\hat{\alpha}^*\phi^* \, d\tau$$

holds.

Unsharp Quantities and Probability

In actual experimental procedures most quantities being measured do not have unique, sharp values. It is therefore necessary to consider the cases involving unsharp quantities.

Let us examine the one-dimensional stationary case where the time-independent factor is

$$\psi = a \sin \frac{2\pi x}{\lambda} \tag{2-8}$$

Note that we have selected a wave type solution. Because solutions are often in wave form the field of quantum mechanics is also known as wave mechanics. Since ψ must be limited to finite values of x, let us say that equation (2-8) holds for $0 < x < L = n\lambda/2$, where n is an integer, and that $\psi = 0$ for $x < 0$

or $x > L$. We must also satisfy the normalizing requirement (2-1). Thus, since $\psi = \psi^*$ in this case, and since L is a multiple of $\lambda/2$,

$$\int_0^L a^2 \sin^2 \frac{2\pi x}{\lambda} \, dx = a^2 \frac{L}{2} = 1 \qquad (2\text{-}9)$$

or $a = \pm\sqrt{2/L}$ (or, if a were complex, $a = e^{i\theta}\sqrt{2/L}$). From this,

$$\psi = \sqrt{\frac{2}{L}} \, e^{i\theta} \sin \frac{2\pi x}{\lambda} \qquad (2\text{-}10)$$

The Hamiltonian operator $\hat{H}$ in this one-dimensional case is given by

$$\hat{H} = -\frac{\hbar^2}{2m} \frac{\partial^2}{\partial x^2} + V$$

Using this equation we find

$$\left(-\frac{\hbar^2}{2m} \frac{\partial^2}{\partial x^2} + V\right)\sqrt{\frac{2}{L}} \, e^{i\theta} \sin \frac{2\pi x}{\lambda} = \left(\frac{\hbar^2}{2m} \frac{4\pi^2}{\lambda^2} + V\right)\sqrt{\frac{2}{L}} \, e^{i\theta} \sin \frac{2\pi x}{\lambda} \qquad (2\text{-}11)$$

The total energy E is seen to be given by the constant coefficient of ψ. Note that the $\sqrt{2/L}\, e^{i\theta}$ is *not* part of the *coefficient* but is part of ψ. Thus

$$E = \frac{\hbar^2}{2m} \frac{4\pi^2}{\lambda^2} + V \qquad (2\text{-}12)$$

or the "classical" kinetic energy is, in this case, expressed by

$$E - V = \frac{1}{2m}\left(\frac{2\pi\hbar}{\lambda}\right)^2 \qquad (2\text{-}13)$$

From classical extrapolation (a poor procedure because it gives the right answer only under special circumstances),

$$E - V = \frac{p_x{}^2}{2m} = \frac{1}{2m}\left(\frac{h}{\lambda}\right)^2 \qquad \text{(as } 2\pi\hbar = h) \qquad (2\text{-}14)$$

and

$$p_x = \pm \frac{h}{\lambda} \qquad (2\text{-}15)$$

This is the usual de Broglie relationship.

If the momentum operator $\hat{p}_x$ is applied to the ψ of (2-10), we find

$$\frac{\hbar}{i} \frac{\partial}{\partial x}\psi = \frac{\hbar}{i}\sqrt{\frac{2}{L}} \, e^{i\theta} \frac{2\pi}{\lambda} \cos \frac{2\pi x}{\lambda} \ne p_x\sqrt{\frac{2}{L}} \, e^{i\theta} \sin \frac{2\pi x}{\lambda}$$

Thus ψ is not an eigenfunction of the operator $\hat{p}_x$ and no sharp value can be expected. The classical extrapolation did not have a sharp, *unique* value either.

We can write equation (2-10) in an exponential form with

$$\psi = \frac{1}{2i}\sqrt{\frac{2}{L}}\left(e^{2\pi i x/\lambda} - e^{-2\pi i x/\lambda}\right)e^{i\theta} \tag{2-16}$$

Now let

$$\psi_1 = \frac{1}{i\sqrt{L}}\,e^{2\pi i x/\lambda} \quad \text{and} \quad \psi_2 = -\frac{1}{i\sqrt{L}}\,e^{-2\pi i x/\lambda}$$

where ψ_1 and ψ_2 are normalized and have the form of monentum eigenfunctions. It can be readily shown that whatever constant value θ assumes in no way influences the following and therefore we will let θ be zero. Equation (2-16) can be seen to be readily put in the form

$$\psi = c_1\psi_1 + c_2\psi_2 \tag{2-17}$$

where c_1 and c_2 are constants. More specifically

$$\psi = \frac{1}{\sqrt{2}}\,\psi_1 + \frac{1}{\sqrt{2}}\,\psi_2.$$

From this we find $c_1 = c_2 = 1/\sqrt{2}$.

Now ψ_1 and ψ_2 satisfy the momentum eigenfunction equation. (We will see later that instead of a single electron eigenfunction, these could represent systems which have, at random, an average of one electron per length L. See Problems 9 and 10 for some limitations.) Also note the particularly interesting feature where the complex conjugate of ψ_2 is involved:

$$\int_0^L \psi_1\psi_2^* \, d\tau = 0$$

If we now use $\hat{p}_x$, we find

$$\hat{p}_x\psi = \frac{1}{\sqrt{2}}\hat{p}_x\psi_1 + \frac{1}{\sqrt{2}}\hat{p}_x\psi_2 = \frac{2\pi\hbar}{\lambda}\left(\frac{1}{\sqrt{2}}\psi_1\right) + \left(-\frac{2\pi\hbar}{\lambda}\right)\left(\frac{1}{\sqrt{2}}\psi_2\right) \tag{2-18}$$

We see from (2-18) that the two components of ψ are individually momentum eigenfunctions although ψ is not. Treated separately, $\hat{p}_x\psi_1 = p_{x1}\psi_1$ and $\hat{p}_x\psi_2 = p_{x2}\psi_2$. The *components* have eigenvalues p_{x1} and p_{x2} of h/λ and $-h/\lambda$, respectively, as just computed from (2-15), where we had assumed a classical relationship. We find that ψ_1 and ψ_2 here are spatially *unique*. These are the only possible components of ψ which are momentum eigenfunctions.

Because of perfect symmetry there can be no preference for one of the eigenvalues over the other; thus both h/λ and $-h/\lambda$ are equally likely to be found by any of the above considerations. We can therefore state that the probability of each is one-half. Now note that the coefficients of ψ_1 and ψ_2 are equal and each is $1/\sqrt{2}$. We can generalize the example as follows:

Let ψ_1 and ψ_2 be eigenfunctions of the operator $\hat{\alpha}$ having eigenvalues α_1 and α_2. If the measurements corresponding to the operator $\hat{\alpha}$ are made on the state represented by

$$\psi = c_1\psi_1 + c_2\psi_2 \qquad (2\text{-}19)$$

the probability of observing α_1 is $c_1^*c_1$ and that of observing α_2 is $c_2^*c_2$.

Postulate VI. A state function can always be expanded uniquely in terms of eigenfunctions of a given operator $\hat{\alpha}$, in the form

$$\phi = \sum_j c_j\psi_j \qquad (2\text{-}20)$$

where the eigenvalues are determined from

$$\hat{\alpha}\psi_j = \alpha_j\psi_j \qquad (2\text{-}21)$$

The probability of observing α_j, when performing the measurement for which $\hat{\alpha}$ is the operator, is $c_j^*c_j$. (All of the ψ_j's must be normalized according to Postulate IV.) Any function that cannot be expanded in this way is not a possible state function.

The *probability* expression indicates that the measured quantities will not have the same value in successive measurements but will be found to be one or the other of the sharp values corresponding to the various components of ψ. Some of the sharp values may occur more often than others. In fact, the *probability* of occurrence is proportional to the square of the magnitude of the coefficient of the sharp value's eigenfunction. In the particular case previously illustrated using the classical approach, each of the two eigenfunctions (for the eigenvalues h/λ and $-h/\lambda$) has $1/\sqrt{2}$ as a coefficient and therefore the two momentum values are equally likely to be the result of experiment. That is, the measured momentum value will have a probability .5 to be directed in the positive x direction and an equal probability of being directed in the negative x direction. The *average value* of the momentum will be zero in this case. This example suggests that *only complex eigenfunctions* yield sharp values of momentum. It should also be clear, therefore, that eigenfunctions themselves are not measurable quantities. The state function, of which $\sqrt{2/L}\sin 2\pi x/\lambda$ is the position dependent factor, has an energy eigenvalue given by equation (2-12). Therefore, as discussed in Chapter I, it must have a time-dependent factor

$$\exp -i\left(\frac{4\pi^2\hbar^2}{2m\lambda^2} + V\right)\frac{t}{\hbar}$$

and thus the complete state function is

$$\psi = \sqrt{\frac{2}{L}}\exp\left[-i\left(\frac{\hbar^2 4\pi^2}{2m\lambda^2} + V\right)\frac{t}{\hbar}\right]\sin\frac{2\pi x}{\lambda} \qquad (2\text{-}22)$$

Note that the time factor is arbitrary to a certain extent since our reference energy for potential is arbitrary. We are interested only in phase or frequency *differences* in utilizing this and, as a result, the arbitrariness will drop out.

A most important characteristic of the Schrödinger equation now becomes apparent. All eigenfunction equations are linear (ψ enters with no higher power than the first) and homogeneous (*each* term has ψ to the first power in it). These equations *do not* have solutions except when the eigenvalues are of a particular set appropriate for the equation in question. If a particular eigenvalue is selected, there may be more than one eigenfunction as a solution. If this is so, it is a mathematical consequence that any linear combination of these solutions is also a solution. The time-dependent Schrödinger equation is very special, however. *Any* linear combination of eigenfunction solutions to the equation, *whether or not they have the same eigenvalues*, are also solutions. This comes about by the relationship between the time-dependent and the spatially dependent factors of the complete eigenfunctions.

PROBLEMS

1. Determine whether the operators

$$\hat{\gamma} = \hat{x}\hat{p}_x = x\,\frac{\hbar}{i}\,\frac{\partial}{\partial x} = \frac{\hbar}{i}\,x\,\frac{\partial}{\partial x} \quad \text{and} \quad \hat{\eta} = \hat{p}_x\hat{x} = \frac{\hbar}{i}\,\frac{\partial}{\partial x}\,x$$

satisfy equation (2-6). It will be shown later (see Problem 2-18) that any eigenfunction can be used in the testing. In a classical situation it is desired to measure momentum times distance, i.e., p times x. What is the correct quantum mechanical operator corresponding to this measurement? Note that $\hat{\beta} = \hat{x}\hat{p}_x - \hat{p}_x\hat{x}$ is a non-zero constant operator. If it were a zero operator $\hat{x}\hat{p}_x$ would be identical with $\hat{p}_x\hat{x}$ and in this case $\hat{x}$ and $\hat{p}_x$ would be said to "commute." Only under this circumstance can the corresponding eigenvalues l (for $\hat{x}$) and p_x (for $\hat{p}_x$), in this case, be found simultaneously.

2. Determine whether kinetic energy and potential energy can be found simultaneously. (Hint: see problem 1 and also note that the potential energy is a function of position and can be evaluated by a suitably chosen power series.)

3. It is given that:

(a) $\hat{\alpha}$ operating on ψ produces an eigenvalue α.

(b) Equation (2-7) holds.

Show that α is real. [*Hint:* Since only one (but any one) eigenvalue is involved, choose $\phi = \psi$.]

4. In the range $a < x < b$ an electronic state function has the spatial form

$$\psi = B \sin \frac{\pi x}{\lambda} + C \sin \frac{2\pi x}{\lambda}$$

The equation for ψ holds in this range but, outside of it, $\psi = 0$.

(a) What discrete values for a and b are possible considering the restrictions of Postulate IV?

(b) What relationship between B and C is imposed by normalization?

(c) Is ψ continuous at $x = a$ and at $x = b$?

5. A time-dependent state function has the form

$$\psi = 3e^{i\beta t} A \sin \frac{2\pi x}{L} + 2Ae^{i\gamma t} \sin \frac{3\pi x}{L}$$

for $-L < x < L$, where $V = V_0$. Outside of this range $V \to \infty$ and $\psi = B$.

(a) Evaluate B.

(b) Which form of Schrödinger's equation must be satisfied by ψ, and why?

(c) Evaluate A, β, and γ.

6. For the state function of Problem 4:

(a) What normalized energy eigenfunctions are involved in the expansion of ψ?

(b) What energies can be measured?

(c) What time dependences have the coefficients of the energy eigenfunctions?

(d) What are the various probabilities associated with the energy measurements?

(e) What are the time dependences of these *probabilities*?

(f) What is the arithmetic mean value of the measured energies? Be sure to consider the probabilities involved.

(g) What are the normalized *momentum* eigenfunctions suitable for the expansion of ψ?

(**h**) What are the corresponding coefficients in their expansion?

(**i**) What are the measured momenta?

(**j**) What are the probabilities associated with measuring the various momenta?

(**k**) What is the mean value of the measured momenta?

7. Answer the questions of Problem 6 in reference to the state function of Problem 5.

8. For a given potential well we will consider two possible state functions. The well is specified by $V \to \infty$ for $x < 0$ and for $x > L$, and by $V = V_0$ for $L > x > 0$. The state functions are

$$\psi_1 = A \sin \frac{3\pi x}{L}$$

and

$$\psi_2 = B \sin \frac{4\pi x}{L}$$

(**a**) Determine A and B, including the time dependence of each.

(**b**) How much energy is needed to transfer the particle from the state represented by ψ_1 to that by ψ_2?

(**c**) What is the *frequency difference* between these two states? This frequency difference may be thought of as a beat frequency.

(**d**) How does $h\Delta\nu = \hbar\Delta\omega$ compare with the energy computed in (**b**)? Note that the light emitted has the beat frequency of the two electronic states involved.

(**e**) How does the potential energy V_0 become involved?

9. Can a state function for the potential well of Problem 8 have the form

$$\psi = A e^{igx} + B e^{i3gx}$$

where g is real and constant? This can be determined by examining the following steps.

Assume that ψ is a state function and that each exponential is an eigenfunction and see if any conflict arises from these assumptions.

(**a**) Determine the relationships between g, A, and L needed to satisfy boundary conditions at $x = 0$ and $x = L$.

(**b**) What are the eigenvalues of energy associated with the eigenfunctions of energy in the expansion of ψ?

(**c**) What must the time dependences of A and B be?

(**d**) Can ψ have suitable values at $x = 0$ and $x = L$ for all values of time so that the requirements of Postulate IV are met?

10. Answer the questions of Problem 9 relative to the state function

$$\psi = Ae^{igx} + Be^{-igx}$$

11. The two state functions of Problem 8 are both eigenfunctions of the Hamiltonian energy operator. Show that the Hermitian condition for $\hat{H}$ holds when these two state functions are used together in the integral.

12. Show that the Hermitian condition, which holds when eigenfunctions of an operator are used, also holds for the momentum operator using the two state functions

$$\phi_1 = Ai \sin \frac{M_1 \pi x}{L}$$

and

$$\phi_2 = B \cos \left(M_2 + \frac{1}{2} \right) \frac{\pi x}{L}$$

where M_1 and M_2 are integers. These forms of state functions hold in the range $L > x > -L$ and the state functions are zero outside of this range. (*Note:* ϕ_1 and ϕ_2 are not momentum eigenfunctions.)

13. A state function is given as

$$\psi = g \left(\frac{3i}{4} \phi_1 + \phi_2 \right)$$

where ϕ_1 and ϕ_2 are energy eigenfunctions given in Problem 12.
(**a**) Show that ϕ_1 and ϕ_2 are satisfactory energy eigenfunctions for the case $V = 0$, $L > x > -L$, and ∞ outside of this range.
(**b**) What are the explicit time-dependent forms of A and B?
(**c**) What are the magnitudes of A and B?
(**d**) What are the probabilities, in a single measurement, of finding the eigenvalue of ϕ_1? of ϕ_2?
(**e**) Over a large number of measurements what is the average value of the energy? Express this in terms of M_1 and M_2.

EXPANSION THEOREMS AND ORTHOGONALITY

We have postulated that any state function can be expanded uniquely in terms of eigenfunctions having sharp eigenvalues and that the probability of occurrence of a particular sharp value was equal to the square of the magnitude of the coefficient of the sharp value's eigenfunction. Here we show how the coefficients and probabilities can be found and we draw a few conclusions.

In our general operator formulation we have

$$\hat{\alpha}\psi_1 = \alpha_1\psi_1 \qquad (2\text{-}23)$$

where $\hat{\alpha}$ could be the operator corresponding to any measurement. Here ψ_1 is the eigenfunction which yields α_1 as the measured value, and

$$\hat{\alpha}^*\psi_2^* = \alpha_2^*\psi_2^* \qquad (2\text{-}24)$$

where it is given that $\alpha_1 \neq \alpha_2$. ($\alpha_2 = \alpha_2^*$, of course, because of the realness of measured quantities.) Multiply equation (2-23) by ψ_2^*. (In doing this ψ_2^* must be written to the left of $\hat{\alpha}$ since otherwise it would indicate that $\hat{\alpha}$ was to operate on ψ_2^* as well as ψ_1. This is *not* the case.) Integrate over all space

$$\int \psi_2^*\hat{\alpha}\psi_1 \, d\tau = \alpha_1 \int \psi_2^*\psi_1 \, d\tau \qquad (2\text{-}25)$$

as α_1 is a constant. Also, because of the Hermitian condition,

$$\int \psi_2^*\hat{\alpha}\psi_1 \, d\tau = \int \psi_1\hat{\alpha}^*\psi_2^* \, d\tau = \alpha_2 \int \psi_1\psi_2^* \, d\tau \qquad (2\text{-}26)$$

because α_2 is real as mentioned previously. Thus

$$\alpha_1 \int \psi_2^*\psi_1 \, d\tau = \alpha_2 \int \psi_1\psi_2^* \, d\tau \qquad (2\text{-}27)$$

Since $\alpha_1 \neq \alpha_2$, however, it is necessary that

$$\int \psi_2^*\psi_1 \, d\tau = 0 \qquad (2\text{-}28)$$

The very important equation (2-28) is called the *orthogonal set relationship*. Members of such sets are *orthogonal*, that is, they satisfy equation (2-28). Thus in general eigenfunctions that yield unequal eigenvalues are orthogonal. (So-called "degenerate" eigenfunctions, which yield the same eigenvalue, can also be expressed in orthogonal terms; thus orthogonality does not imply unequal eigenvalues.) Note that the eigenfunctions of equation (2-17) were orthogonal and their momentum eigenvalues were unequal, but their energy eigenvalues are equal.

Let us assume a state function ϕ (Greek phi) which, according to Postulate VI, can be stated as a sum of eigenfunctions ψ_i (for which $\hat{\alpha}\psi_i = \alpha_i\psi_i$). Then we can state

$$\phi = \sum_{i=1}^{\infty} c_i\psi_i \qquad (2\text{-}29)$$

Here ψ_i is the complete eigenfunction (including time dependence) but in the expansion process we integrate over space only. The time-dependent factors remain unaltered in the integration; because of the form of the time dependences it does not enter in the determination of coefficients when the expansion is in terms of energy eigenfunctions. Multiply by any ψ_j^* and integrate over space:

$$\int \psi_j^* \phi \, d\tau = \sum_{i=1}^{\infty} c_i \int \psi_j^* \psi_i \, d\tau \qquad (2\text{-}30)$$

But

$$\int \psi_j^* \psi_i \, d\tau = \delta(i,j) \qquad (2\text{-}31)$$

where $\delta(i,j) = 0$ for $i \neq j$ [from (2-28)] and $\delta(i,j) = 1$ for $i = j$ [from the normalizing condition (2-1)]. Thus all terms of the summation except the one involving $i = j$ drop out, and

$$\int \psi_j^* \phi \, d\tau = c_j \qquad (2\text{-}32)$$

where, as previously mentioned, ψ_j is time dependent. In finding c_j, however, $\psi_j \psi_j^*$ is involved. This product has no time dependence because of the way time enters eigenfunctions. As a result c_j is also independent of time. The expansions are therefore time dependent only through the time-dependent factor in the eigenfunction. Thus we have a way of finding the coefficients of the expansion. Note in particular that ϕ could represent *any* state function. Note also the analogy to ordinary Fourier expansion and that the methods must be alike because sines, and so on, are also eigenfunctions in certain situations.

Let us consider $\int \phi \phi^* \, d\tau$:

$$\phi^* = \sum_{k=1}^{\infty} c_k^* \psi_k^*, \qquad \phi = \sum_{j=1}^{\infty} c_j \psi_j \qquad (2\text{-}33)$$

$$\int \phi \phi^* \, d\tau = \sum_{j=1}^{\infty} \sum_{k=1}^{\infty} c_j c_k^* \int \psi_k^* \psi_j \, d\tau = 1 \qquad (2\text{-}34)$$

by the normalizing condition. Again, for $k \neq j$, the integral in the summation is zero; for $k = j$, the integral in the summation is unity. Thus

$$\int \phi \phi^* \, d\tau = \sum_{j=1}^{\infty} c_j c_j^* = 1 \qquad (2\text{-}35)$$

This says that the sum of the squares of the magnitudes of the components of a normalized state function is unity. The components can be thought of as being at right angles in a function space and the sum of their squares is the hypotenuse. This right angle concept is the basis for the application of the term " orthogonal " to the set.

But, by Postulate VI, $c_j c_j^*$ is the probability of finding the eigenvalue α_j. Thus the sum of the probabilities of finding one value or another as a result of a single experiment is unity as expected.

Charge Density by Orthogonal Expansion

" Charge density " due to a single electron must really be proportional to the probability of finding the electron at the position for which knowledge of the charge density is desired. Therefore we must apply the eigenfunction equation for which the operator is the position operator $\hat{x}$. Then the *eigenfunctions* ψ_l must be delta functions and the eigenvalues are the sharp values l. This can be seen by equation (1-8):

$$\hat{x}\psi_l = l\psi_l \tag{1-8}$$

This equation is only possible if ψ_l is zero at other than $x = l$, as explained earlier. When the eigenfunctions have the form of $\delta(x - s_1)$ of equation (1-11), it is easily shown that they are also orthogonal. Unless the s values are the same in two δ's, their product is zero everywhere. But when they have the same s value their product integrates to one. Then, clearly, this strange set of functions are eigenfunctions and can be used for expansion. They can, in fact, be used in the expansion of any desired state function. These position eigenfunctions are the ones to be used in the determination of the probability of finding the particle at any position, l, a sharp value of $\hat{x}$.

We now examine crudely some of the characteristics of $\phi\phi^*$ when the state function and its complex conjugate are each expressed in expansions of these delta function position eigenfunctions. First, only one eigenfunction at a position is involved in the integration of $\phi\phi^*$.

Since $\phi = \sum_j c_j \psi_j$ and $\phi^* = \sum_k c_k^* \psi_k^*$,

$$\phi^*\phi = \sum_j \sum_k c_k^* c_j \psi_j \psi_k^*$$

But, for $j \neq k$, $\psi_j \psi_k^* = 0$ since either one or the other is zero. That is, ψ_l is infinite only at $x = l$ and zero for all other values. Thus, if the integration is limited to an infinitesimal space in the neighborhood of l, we have only one term of the summation:

$$\int_{l-dl/2}^{l+dl/2} \phi\phi^* \, dx = \int_{l-dl/2}^{l+dl/2} (\psi_l \psi_l^* \, dx) c_l c_l^* \tag{2-36}$$

all other terms on the right-hand side ($\psi_l^*\psi_m$, $\psi_n^*\psi_m$, $\psi_n^*\psi_n$, etc.) being zero in the interval $l - dl/2$ to $l + dl/2$. But in this set of eigenfunctions

$$\int_{l-dl/2}^{l+dl/2} \psi_l \psi_l^* \, dx = 1 \tag{2-37}$$

Therefore

$$\int_{l-dl/2}^{l+dl/2} \phi\phi^* \, dx = c_l c_l^* \tag{2-38}$$

But $c_l c_l^*$ is, according to our previous work, the probability of finding that the particle has the position $x = l \pm dl/2$. The integral on the left is therefore the probability of finding the particle between $l - dl/2$ and $l + dl/2$. The integral itself is just $\phi(l)\phi^*(l) \, dl$ which, by Postulate VI is the probability of finding the electron in a "volume" element dl. Now $\phi\phi^*$ is called the *probability density* since multiplying it by the volume element dl results in the actual probability involved. Thus $q\phi\phi^*$ is a charge density averaged over time, where q is the electronic charge.

The Mean Value Theorem; The Expectation Value

We wish to demonstrate a method of obtaining a mean value for a measurement (symbolized by the operator $\hat{\alpha}$) on a system symbolized by state function ψ. When actual physical measurements are being made there are many things that produce slight disturbances of the system under observation. As a result the sharp values discussed up to this point are essentially never measured. The disturbances result in small variations from one observed event to the next so that we average the observations as part of our measuring technique. The average or "mean" value is the expected result of physical measurement. The direct method of computing the mean value thus has special importance.

Since measurements are not reproducible, the measurements are clearly not unique and therefore the state function could not be an eigenfunction. Therefore

$$\hat{\alpha}\psi \neq \alpha\psi \tag{2-39}$$

Let ϕ_m be a set of eigenfunctions for the operator $\hat{\alpha}$. That is,

$$\hat{\alpha}\phi_m = \alpha_m \phi_m \tag{2-40}$$

where α_m is the eigenvalue corresponding to ϕ_m. We next expand the state function ψ in terms of the eigenfunctions ϕ_m:

$$\psi = \sum_m c_m \phi_m \tag{2-41}$$

The coefficients c_m are obtained by the use of the orthogonality condition:

$$\int \phi_m \phi_n^* \, d\tau = \delta(m, n) = \begin{cases} 0, & m \neq n \\ 1, & m = n \end{cases} \tag{2-42}$$

To use this, multiply both sides of equation (2-41) by ϕ_n^* and integrate over all available space. We then [as in (2-32)] obtain

$$c_n = \int \phi_n^* \psi \, d\tau \tag{2-43}$$

These coefficients are important in that, by Postulate VI, $c_n c_n^*$ is the probability of measuring α_n, the eigenvalue of ϕ_n, when observing the system having state function ψ.

We can now expand $\hat{\alpha}\psi$ by making use of the fact that ϕ_m is an eigenfunction with eigenvalue α_m. Operating on equation (2-41) with

$$\hat{\alpha}\psi = \sum_m c_m \hat{\alpha}\phi_m \tag{2-44}$$

we use (2-40) to obtain

$$\hat{\alpha}\psi = \sum_m c_m \alpha_m \phi_m \tag{2-45}$$

Both sides of this equation are multiplied by ψ^*; but on the right-hand side ψ^* is expressed in terms of the ϕ^*s:

$$\psi^* \hat{\alpha}\psi = \left(\sum_n c_n^* \phi_n^* \right) \sum_m c_m \alpha_m \phi_m$$

Both sides of the equation are then integrated over all space as shown in equation (2-46), where $d\tau$ is an element of volume:

$$\int \psi^* \hat{\alpha}\psi \, d\tau = \int \left(\sum_n c_n^* \phi_n^* \right)\left(\sum_m c_m \alpha_m \phi_m \right) d\tau \tag{2-46}$$

The integrand on the right-hand side is a product and this can be expanded:

$$\int \psi^* \hat{\alpha}\psi \, d\tau = \sum_m \sum_n c_n^* c_m \alpha_m \int \phi_n^* \phi_m \, d\tau \tag{2-47}$$

Then, because of the orthogonal functions used, terms for which $n \neq m$ drop out, and

$$\int \psi^* \hat{\alpha}\psi \, d\tau = \sum_m c_m^* c_m \alpha_m \tag{2-48}$$

Note that each eigenvalue is weighted in this sum by the probability of its occurrence. In N measurements (N large) $Nc_k c_k^*$ is the expected number of times that the value α_k will appear. Therefore the arithmetic average, $\langle \alpha \rangle$, of the values found by experiment is

$$\langle \alpha \rangle = \sum_n c_n^* c_n \alpha_n \tag{2-49}$$

The symbol $\langle\ \rangle$ is used to designate arithmetic average. From equation (2-48),

$$\langle \alpha \rangle = \int \psi^* \hat{\alpha} \psi \, d\tau \tag{2-50}$$

We therefore can obtain an *average* value without obtaining any of the specific values. In many instances, *only* the average is of interest. When a large number of values near some central value are measured, the average value *is* the one of interest and it is known as the *expectation value*.

In our previous case involving momentum [see (2-13) to (2-18)] p_x was found to be either $\pm 2\pi\hbar/\lambda$ with equal likelihood and therefore it is clear that the average is zero. The state function was

$$\psi = \sqrt{\frac{2}{L}} \sin \frac{\pi x}{\lambda} \tag{2-51}$$

We can test this easily. Here $\psi^* = \psi$ because ψ is real in this case. Since the momentum operator is $(\hbar/i)(\partial/\partial x)$,

$$\langle p_x \rangle = \frac{2}{L} \int_0^L \left(\sin \frac{\pi x}{\lambda} \right) \left(\frac{\hbar\pi}{i\lambda} \right) \left(\cos \frac{\pi x}{\lambda} \right) dx \tag{2-52}$$

$$\langle p_x \rangle = \frac{\pi\hbar}{i\lambda L} \int_0^L \sin \frac{2\pi x}{\lambda} \, dx = 0 \tag{2-53}$$

This checks our previous conclusion.

PROBLEMS

14. Two energy eigenfunctions for the region $0 < x < L$ are

$$\psi_a = A \sin \frac{9\pi x}{L}$$

and

$$\psi_b = B \sin \frac{10\pi x}{L}$$

The coefficients A and B are time dependent. Show the time dependence of each and show that ψ_a and ψ_b are orthogonal at all times.

15. For the range $0 < x < L$, where $V = V_0$, the state function has the spatial dependence, at time $t = 0$, of

$$\phi = A \sin^2 \frac{\pi x}{L}$$

and, for $x < 0$ and for $x > L$, $\phi = 0$ and $V = \infty$.

(a) Evaluate A (ϕ must be normalized.)

(b) Determine the energy eigenfunctions suitable for the region $L > x > 0$ making the assumption for now (see Chapter III) that the eigenfunctions are zero outside this range. Be sure to normalize them.

(c) Expand ϕ in terms of these *eigenfunctions*, determining the expansion coefficients as in equation (2-32).

(d) What are the probabilities of measuring various energies?

(e) What is the expected average energy measured after a number of determinations?

16. What is the momentum expectation value for the state function $\psi = Ae^{igx} + Be^{-igx}$? What must be the ratio A/B for this to be a state function? Here $V = V_0$ for $L > x > 0$ and $V = \infty$ outside of this range.

17. Two energy eigenfunctions appropriate to simple harmonic motion, with g real and constant, are

$$\psi_A = Ae^{-x^2 g}$$

and

$$\psi_B = Bxe^{-x^2 g}$$

(*Hint*: Pay particular attention to odd and even symmetry.)

(a) Show that ψ_A and ψ_B are orthogonal over the range $\infty > x > -\infty$.

(b) Does the Hermitian condition hold for $\hat{p}_x$ for every combination of these functions?

(c) What are the momentum expectation values?

(d) What must be the x dependence of the potential energy?

(e) Does the Hermitian condition hold for $\hat{H}$ for every combination of the ψ's?

18. Postulate V, the Hermitan condition, is stated to be a limitation on operators. It utilizes eigenfunctions of the operator, however, and these cannot be found until the proper operator is established. As a way out of this dilemma show that the Hermitian condition holds for *any* function satisfying Postulate VI if it holds for any complete set of eigenfunctions of the operator involved and thus it can be tested on any such function. (*Hint*: Let

$$\phi^* = \sum c_k^* \theta_k^*$$

and

$$\psi = \sum b_j \theta_j$$

where the θs are a set of eigenfunctions of the operator $\hat{\alpha}$ for which the Hermitian condition holds. That is, $\hat{\alpha}^* \theta_j^* = \alpha_j \theta_j^*$, etc.)

19. A system is described by a state function ψ and it is desired to find the distribution of momenta for this state. In order to do this we must find the probabilities associated with the various momenta and this means that we must find the coefficients in an expansion in terms of momentum eigenfunctions (which are always of the form $\phi = e^{ip_x x/\hbar}$). Thus, according to equation (2-32),

$$b \int \phi^* e^{-ipx/\hbar}\, d\tau = c(p)$$

where b is a normalizing constant and $c(p)c^*(p)$ is our desired probability. Here $d\tau = dx$, of course. It is clear that $c(p)$ really is a function of p as indicated symbolically.

Use the fact that $c(p)$ bears a resemblance to the Fourier transform of ψ. Show that we can find ψ from a known $c(p)$ and that therefore $c(p)$ must also have some of the properties of a state function.

20. Find the momentum expectation value when the state function is given by

$$\psi = A e^{ip_z x/\hbar} e^{-(x-x_0)^2/4\sigma}$$

21. What is the probability of observing a momentum $(-g)$ for a system having the state function

$$\psi = T\left[\cos\frac{gx}{\hbar} + \sin\frac{gx}{\hbar}\right]$$

22. A potential well has infinite barriers at $x = L$ and $-L$ and, between the limits $L > x > -L$ the potential is zero. Can a function defined in this range at time $t = 0$ by

$$\psi = a\left(\sin\frac{3\pi x}{L}\right)e^{2\pi i x/L}$$

be a state function? Does it meet the requirements of Postulate VI and the boundary conditions?

  (a) Expand into energy eigenfunctions (for the complete Hamiltonian). Are functions of the form $e^{n\pi i x/L}$ eigenfunctions of the Hamiltonian everywhere?

  (b) Indicate any time-dependent factors explicitly.

  (c) Does this function satisfy the state function boundary conditions at all times? Demonstrate your statement.

23. A state function is given by

$$\psi = 0.3\phi_1 + 0.4i\phi_2 + 0.5\phi_3 - 0.7i\phi_4 + 0.1\phi_5$$

The ϕs are eigenfunctions of both momentum and energy.

(a) Assuming that all functions are normalized, is the set of coefficients self-consistent? Show.

(b) The corresponding momentum eigenvalues are $p_1 = 1$, $p_2 = -1.5$, $p_3 = 2$, $p_4 = -2$, $p_5 = 2.5$. What is the expectation value of the momentum? Units are 10^{-28} kg·m/sec.

(c) The corresponding energy eigenvalues are $E_1 = 2$, $E_2 = 3.25$, $E_3 = E_4 = 5$, $E_5 = 7.25$. What is the expectation value of the energy? Units are 10^{-26} J.

24. Use symmetry arguments here. Do not integrate.

(a) Two functions are given for the range $L > x > -L$:

$$\theta_1 = x \sin \frac{2\pi x^2}{L^2} \quad \text{and} \quad \theta_2 = x^2 \sin \frac{2\pi x}{L}$$

State whether you think θ_1 and θ_2 are orthogonal and your reasons for so concluding.

(b) Repeat (a) for

$$\theta_1 = x \sin \frac{2\pi x^2}{L^2} \quad \text{and} \quad \theta_2 = x \sin \frac{2\pi x}{L}$$

SUMMARY OF POSTULATES*

I. There exists a state function that contains all possible information about the system.

II. For every physical measurement there exists a mathematical operator. Some of the operators are:

$$\hat{p}_x = \frac{\hbar}{i} \frac{\partial}{\partial x} \qquad \hat{V} = V$$

$$\hat{E} = -\frac{\hbar}{i} \frac{\partial}{\partial t} \qquad \hat{x} = x$$

Operators are used on the state function ψ and sharp values result if, and only if

$$\hat{\alpha}\psi = \alpha\psi$$

where α is a (real) constant, the measured value, called the eigenvalue. State functions satisfying this equation are called eigenfunctions.

* Includes two additional postulates.

III. Operators for other than in Postulate **II** are formed by: (a) expressing the measured quantities classically in terms of the previously defined quantities with defined operators, and (b) substituting the operators for the classical quantities. All newly found operators (e.g., the Hamiltonian) must satisfy Postulate **V**.

$$E = \tfrac{1}{2}m(V_x{}^2 + V_y{}^2 + V_z{}^2) + V = \frac{1}{2m}(p_x{}^2 + p_y{}^2 + p_z{}^2) + V$$

Then

$$\hat{E} = -\frac{\hbar^2}{2m}\left(\frac{\partial^2}{\partial x^2} + \frac{\partial^2}{\partial y^2} + \frac{\partial^2}{\partial z^2}\right) + V = \hat{H} \text{ (the Hamiltonian)}$$

(frequently reserved
for time derivative
above)

IV. State functions are subject to the following restrictions
   (a) They must be finite and continuous (except for eigenfunctions, which may be infinite or discontinuous at a finite number of points).
   (b) They must be single valued.
   (c) $\int \psi\psi^* \, d\tau = 1$ (the "normalizing" condition).
   (d) ψ must go to zero at infinity.
   Also see Postulate **VI**.
V. Given any two eigenfunctions ψ and ϕ of the quantum mechanical operator $\hat{\alpha}$, the Hermitian condition,

$$\int \phi^* \hat{\alpha}\psi \, d\tau = \int \psi\hat{\alpha}^*\phi^* \, d\tau$$

holds.
VI. A state function can always be expanded uniquely in terms of eigenfunctions of a given operator $\hat{\alpha}$ in the form

$$\phi = \sum_j c_j \psi_j$$

where the eigenvalues are determined from

$$\hat{\alpha}\psi_j = \alpha_j \psi_j$$

The probability of observing α_j when performing the measurement for which $\hat{\alpha}$ is the operator is $c_j c_j^*$. (ϕ and all of the ψ_js must be normalized according to Postulate **IV**.) Any function that cannot be expanded in this way is not a possible state function.

Two additional postulates are needed.

VII. Each electron has a *spin* which can be in either of two states that are designated with positive or negative signs. Two states otherwise identical but with different spins are different. Two states having the same spatial and time dependence are different only because of spin. Thus "spin" should be considered as part of the state function. (It is not a function of time or position.) All of the eigenfunctions in the expansion of a state function of a single particle must be of the same spin (as the particle itself).

VIII. (Pauli's exclusion principle) No two electrons can occupy the same state (have the same state function). Thus when the lowest two levels are occupied, further electrons must go into states of higher energy.

III

BOUNDARY CONDITIONS AND QUANTUM MECHANICS EXAMPLES

Since real systems are confined in space by one means or another, and since interfaces exist between two materials (like the surface between air and glass), we must consider the transition that confines certain physical properties to limited volumes. The transition regions are most frequently expressed in terms of potential energy changes, sometimes by abrupt changes for simplification. The rules of quantum mechanics must hold even in these transition regions. We begin by discussing the conditions imposed on our eigenfunctions by potential changes that bound a region.

BOUNDARIES AND POTENTIAL VARIATIONS

Let us look at a one-dimensional system in which x is the spatial variable. Consider a region of length L in which the potential for an electron is some arbitrary value V_0. The potential goes very rapidly to infinity for $x > L$ or $x < 0$. This is a classical case of confining the electron to the region for $0 < x < L$. As we move along x from minus infinity to plus infinity, we sense that the potential energy is infinite except in a small region of length L. The Schrödinger equation holds everywhere along x but we must remember, now, that V is a function of x. For values of x where V is infinite, if any stationary states exist, we have,

$$-\frac{\hbar^2}{2m}\frac{\partial^2\psi}{\partial x^2} + \infty\psi = E\psi \tag{3-1}$$

It is clear that ψ must be zero in this region, or E infinite, to satisfy this equation, and the latter is unreal.

For values of x between zero and L, however, we have

$$-\frac{\hbar^2}{2m}\frac{\partial^2\psi}{\partial x^2} + V_0\psi = E\psi \qquad (3\text{-}2)$$

Let us try a solution of the type

$$\psi = T\sin(bx + c) \qquad (3\text{-}3)$$

where T, b, and c are constants, that is, are independent of x. Now T is presumably a function of time. Then differentiating twice and replacing $T\sin(bx + c)$ in the expression with ψ, we have

$$\frac{\partial^2\psi}{\partial x^2} = -\psi b^2 \qquad (3\text{-}4)$$

Putting this in our differential equation, we have

$$\frac{\hbar^2 b^2}{2m}\psi + V_0\psi = E\psi \qquad (3\text{-}5)$$

and therefore

$$E = V_0 + \frac{\hbar^2 b^2}{2m} \qquad (3\text{-}6)$$

or

$$E - V_0 = \frac{\hbar^2 b^2}{2m} \qquad (3\text{-}7)$$

The form (3-3) of the solution for ψ is clearly proper where $0 < x < L$ and clearly not proper outside of this range where we know ψ must be zero. The eigenfunction, then, must have different analytic forms for inside and outside the "box."

What about the situation *at $x = 0$* and *at $x = L$*? Let us examine a small neighborhood around these points. The equation involves a second derivative, and derivatives are defined as limits, so

$$\frac{\partial^2\psi}{\partial x^2} = \lim_{\Delta x \to 0}\frac{\Delta(\partial\psi/\partial x)}{\Delta x} \qquad (3\text{-}8)$$

Hence, in the limit,

$$-\frac{\hbar^2}{2m}\frac{\Delta(\partial\psi/\partial x)}{\Delta x} + V\psi = E\psi \qquad (3\text{-}9)$$

or

$$\frac{\hbar^2}{2m} \Delta \frac{\partial \psi}{\partial x} = (V - E)\psi \, \Delta x \qquad (3\text{-}10)$$

In real systems there are no abrupt changes in potential energy—all real systems change gradually if we take the scale fine enough. In a small region near the boundaries, therefore, V may be very large but still finite. Then, as Δx goes to zero, so does the whole right-hand side of the equation. Thus the incremental change in $\partial \psi / \partial x$ must also be zero. Thus there is *no abrupt change in $\partial \psi / \partial x$* in real systems and therefore ψ *itself must be continuous*.

As V gets more and more abrupt in its change, we still want the results obtained from the preceding physical considerations to hold; that is, we must at least have ψ continuous, even though $\partial \psi / \partial x$ will, in the limit of an abrupt change in V to *infinity*, be allowed to be discontinuous. Abrupt *finite* changes in V will still require that $\partial \psi / \partial x$ be continuous.

Conclusion. At boundaries between regions ψ is continuous; $\partial \psi / \partial x$ also is continuous for *finite* potential changes.

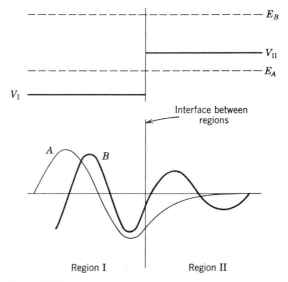

Fig. 3-1 Interfaces and Eigenfunctions. The potential energy is higher in region II than in region I. Two state functions ψ_A and ψ_B are shown, where $E_B > V_{II} > E_A > V_I$. The boundary conditions both for ψ_A and ψ_B at the limits of regions I and II yield: $\psi_I = \psi_{II}$, $\dfrac{\partial \psi_I}{\partial x} = \dfrac{\partial \psi_{II}}{\partial x}$.

Thus in our example, since $\psi = 0$ for $x < 0$ and for $x > L$, in order that ψ be continuous, it must also be zero at the points $x = 0$ and $x = L$. Then our function $\psi = T \sin(bx + c)$ is too general. We must have $\psi = 0$ at the boundary $x = 0$. Thus

$$0 = T \sin(0 + c)$$

$$\sin c = 0 \tag{3-11}$$

Thus, from (3-11),

$$c = n\pi, \qquad n \text{ an integer} \tag{3-12}$$

and at the boundary $x = L$,

$$\sin(bL + n\pi) = 0 \tag{3-13}$$

now, from (3-13),

$$bL + n\pi = m\pi, \qquad m \text{ an integer} \tag{3-14}$$

This, of course, means that

$$bL = k\pi \tag{3-15}$$

where k must be an integer since it is the difference between integers. Thus for our solution to fit all physical limitations, it must have the form

$$\psi = T \sin \frac{\pi k x}{L} \tag{3-16}$$

Note that c has been left out. If n were an even integer, then $\sin(bx + n\pi) = \sin bx$. If n were odd, $\sin(bx + n\pi) = -\sin bx$, which is equivalent to changing the sign of T. This fits the general condition that a second-order equation in x can have *only two* arbitrary constants (independent of x). Even though T is a function of time, it is a constant in x.

We can evaluate the magnitude of T by the normalizing condition:

$$\int_{-\infty}^{\infty} \psi\psi^* \, dx = 1 \tag{3-17}$$

In the regions for $x < 0$ and $x > L$ the eigenfunction is zero and therefore it does not contribute to the integral. Thus

$$TT^* \int_0^L \sin^2\left(\frac{\pi k}{L} x\right) dx = 1 \tag{3-18}$$

Without bothering to look up the integral, it should be remembered that the average value of $\sin^2$ over any integral number of half-cycles is one-half. This is easily seen as

$$\sin^2 x + \cos^2 x = 1$$

and the average values of $\sin^2 x$ and $\cos^2 x$ are the same over half-cycles. Therefore each averages to one-half. Then

$$TT^* \int_0^L \sin^2 \frac{\pi k x}{L} \, dx = \frac{L}{2} \, TT^* = 1 \qquad (3\text{-}19)$$

Now

$$T^*T = \frac{2}{L}, \qquad T = \mathscr{T} \sqrt{\frac{2}{L}}$$

where $\mathscr{T}$ is a function of time such that

$$\mathscr{T}\mathscr{T}^* = 1$$

Thus

$$\text{for } x < 0 \qquad \psi_k = 0$$

$$\text{for } L > x > 0 \qquad \psi_k = \mathscr{T} \sqrt{\frac{2}{L}} \sin \frac{\pi k x}{L} \qquad (3\text{-}20)$$

$$\text{for } x > L \qquad \psi_k = 0$$

We have put a subscript k on ψ to indicate that this ψ goes with k in the analytic expression. Note that the eigenvalue of energy is given by

$$E_k = V_0 + \frac{\hbar^2}{2m}\left(\frac{k\pi}{L}\right)^2 \qquad (3\text{-}21)$$

Not all energy values are possible since k is an integer. We previously showed that the complete eigenfunction had a time-dependent factor $e^{-iEt/\hbar}$. Thus

$$\mathscr{T}_k = \exp - \frac{iE_k t}{\hbar} \qquad (3\text{-}22)$$

This satisfies the requirement previously imposed that $\mathscr{T}\mathscr{T}^* = 1$. Since V_0 is arbitrary, so is E_k and thus so is the "rotational" velocity of $\mathscr{T}_k$. But the rotational velocity itself does not appear in the form of a measurable quantity—an eigenvalue—and thus the expression itself is not measurable. Absolute energy values cannot be measured, only the differences are measurable and then the *potential energy and all arbitrariness* drops out. The ψ_ks equal zero for $x < 0$ or $x > L$. The functional forms of ψ_k for $L > x > 0$ and the eigenvalues E_k are given for selected k values in Table 3-1.

Here E_1 is the lowest energy state. Note that E_1 *is not* V_0, that even in the

TABLE 3-1

k	ψ_k	E_k
0	no eigenfunction	—
1	$\mathcal{T}_1 \sqrt{\dfrac{2}{L}} \sin \dfrac{\pi}{L}$	$V_0 + U_0$
2	$\mathcal{T}_2 \sqrt{\dfrac{2}{L}} \sin 2 \dfrac{\pi x}{L}$	$V_0 + 4U_0$
3	$\mathcal{T}_3 \sqrt{\dfrac{2}{L}} \sin 3 \dfrac{\pi x}{L}$	$V_0 + 9U_0$
5	$\mathcal{T}_5 \sqrt{\dfrac{2}{L}} \sin 5 \dfrac{\pi x}{L}$	$V_0 + 25U_0$
10	$\mathcal{T}_{10} \sqrt{\dfrac{2}{L}} \sin 10 \dfrac{\pi x}{L}$	$V_0 + 100U_0$

Note: $U_0 = \pi^2 \hbar^2 / 2mL^2$.

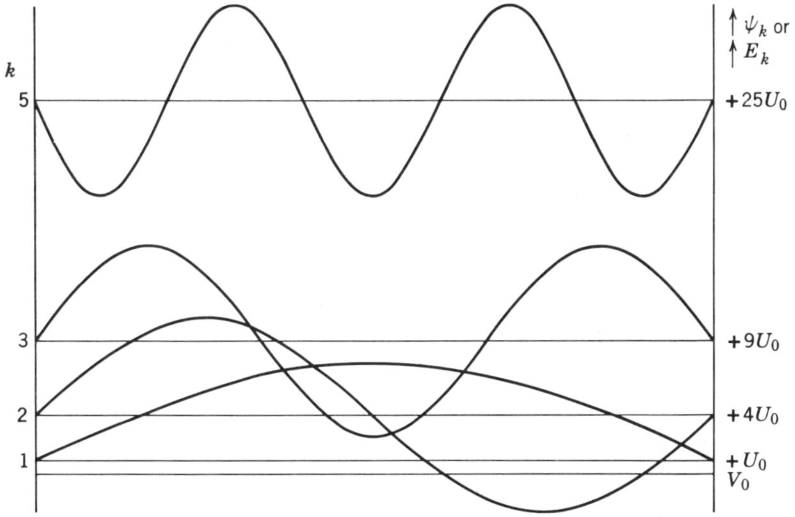

Fig. 3-2 ψ_k drawn with energy diagram. For clarity, each ψ_k is drawn with E_k as its x-axis.

lowest state some "kinetic" energy is involved. The energy required to raise the particle (e.g., electron) from the $k = 1$ state to, say, the $k = 3$ state, is measurable and equals $8\hbar^2\pi^2/2mL^2$. Note that V_0 has dropped out.

To get some ideas of magnitudes:

For $L = 1\text{Å}(10^{-8} \text{ cm}, 10^{-10}\text{m})$

$$E_1 = 5.95 \times 10^{-17} \text{ J} + V_0$$
$$= 371 \text{ eV} + V_0$$

where eV stands for electron volt, the kinetic energy acquired by an electron in falling through 1V of potential difference in a vacuum.

For $L = 1$ cm $(10^{-2}$ m):

$$E_1 = 3.71 \times 10^{-14} \text{ eV} + V_0$$
$$E_{10^4} = 3.71 \times 10^{-6} \text{ eV} + V_0$$
$$E_{10^7} = 3.71 \text{ eV} + V_0$$
$$E_{10^8} = 371 \text{ eV} + V_0$$

Note that the *highest* level for any of 10^8 electrons in 1 cm is the same as the level when one electron is restricted to 10^{-8} cm. Compare this with the remark following equation (3-58).

A TRANSITION

The second example we consider has some aspects of the one just discussed. We will assume that an electron is in a potential "box," as in the last example. The well has potential barriers at $x = 0$ and $x = L$. The particle is assumed to be in the $k = 1$ state given by the state function $_1\psi_1$ (the meaning of the leading subscript will be clarified later):

$$x < 0, \qquad _1\psi_1 = 0$$

$$L > x > 0, \qquad _1\psi_1 = \sqrt{\frac{2}{L}}\left\{\exp -\frac{it}{\hbar}\left[V_0 + \frac{\hbar^2\pi^2}{2mL^2}\right]\right\}\sin\frac{\pi x}{L} \qquad (3\text{-}23)$$

$$x > L, \qquad _1\psi_1 = 0$$

At time $t = 0$ (an arbitrary time in an infinite world that goes back to $t = -\infty$), the wall at $x = L$ is very rapidly moved to the position $x = 2L$. This may take some energy away from or may add some to the electron in the well. Now we ask, "What is the new state of the electron?"

First, at time $t = 0 +$, the state function, now designated $_2\psi$, must be just what it is at $t = 0 -$ as any discontinuous change in the state function with time corresponds to an infinite energy. Second, the old state function was an eigenfunction of the old system, but it is not an eigenfunction of the new system.

Eigenfunctions of the new system are of the following form:

$$0 > x, \qquad _2\psi_n = 0$$

$$2L > x > 0, \qquad _2\psi_n = \sqrt{\frac{1}{L}}\left\{\exp -\frac{it}{\hbar}\left[V_0 + \frac{\hbar^2\pi^2n^2}{8mL^2}\right]\right\}\sin\frac{\pi n x}{2L} \qquad (3\text{-}24)$$

$$x > 2L, \qquad _2\psi_n = 0$$

Note that all $_2\psi_n$ in the expansion must have the same spin as $_1\psi_1$ according to Postulate VII.

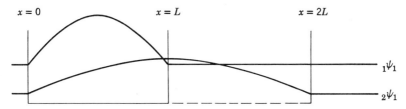

$x = 0$ $x = L$ $x = 2L$

$_1\psi_1$

$_2\psi_1$

Fig. 3-3 "Box" goes from $x = 0$ to $x = L$ at $t < 0$. For $t > 0$, limits are 0 and $2L$.

In Fig. 3-3 eigenvalues are

$$_2E_n = V_0 + \frac{\hbar^2\pi^2n^2}{8mL^2},$$

the value in square brackets of (3-24). The "leading" subscript indicates that the quantity is related to the second condition of the potential well.

The state function at time $t = 0$, however, is unchanged by this sudden move. Since the state function must be expressible as the sum of (the new) eigenfunctions, at $t = 0$, between the limits $L > x > 0$, we have,

$$_2\psi = \sqrt{\frac{2}{L}}\sin\frac{\pi x}{L} = \sum {_2c_n}\sqrt{\frac{1}{L}}\sin\frac{\pi n x}{2L} \qquad (3\text{-}25)$$

and, for x greater than L (especially between L and $2L$), we have

$$_2\psi = 0 = \sum {_2c_n}\sqrt{\frac{1}{L}}\sin\frac{\pi n x}{2L} \qquad (3\text{-}26)$$

The new eigenfunctions, however, are nonzero between 0 and $2L$.

Following our prescribed rules of expansion, we multiply both sides by one of our new eigenfunctions (spatial part only as $t = 0$) and integrate over all space. Both systems are zero outside the range 0 to $2L$, so there will be no contribution to the integral from those regions. From equation (3-26) we conclude that the left-hand integral should extend only to L:

$$\sqrt{\frac{2}{L}}\sqrt{\frac{1}{L}}\int_0^L \sin\frac{\pi x}{L}\sin\frac{l\pi x}{2L}\,dx = \sum \frac{{}_2c_n}{L}\int_0^{2L}\sin\frac{\pi l x}{2L}\sin\frac{\pi n x}{2L}\,dx \qquad (3\text{-}27)$$

On the right side all integrals $n \neq l$ are zero. For $n = l$ we have a value of L for the integral (average value of $1/2$ over distance $2L$). Thus the right side simply becomes ${}_2c_l$. Then

$$\frac{\sqrt{2}}{L}\int_0^L \sin\frac{\pi x}{L}\sin\frac{\pi l x}{2L}\,dx = {}_2c_l \qquad (3\text{-}28)$$

For $l = 2$ this is simply the integral of $\sin^2 \pi x/L$. We then have

$$\frac{\sqrt{2}}{L}\frac{L}{2} = {}_2c_2 = \frac{\sqrt{2}}{2} \qquad (3\text{-}29)$$

or

$$_2c_2{}^2 = .5$$

For l even, but not 2, the integral is zero. For l odd:

$$I_l = \int_0^L \sin\frac{\pi x}{L}\sin\frac{\pi l x}{2L}\,dx = \frac{L}{\pi}\int_0^\pi \sin y \sin\left(\frac{l}{2}y\right)dy \qquad (3\text{-}30)$$

where $y = \pi x/L$. By a trigonometric identity,

$$I_l = \frac{L}{2\pi}\int_0^\pi \left\{\cos\left(\frac{l}{2}+1\right)y - \cos\left(\frac{l}{2}-1\right)y\right\}dy \qquad (3\text{-}31)$$

$$I_l = \frac{L}{2\pi}\left\{\frac{\sin((l/2)+1)y}{l/2+1}\right]_0^\pi - \frac{\sin((l/2)-1)y}{l/2-1}\right]_0^\pi\right\} \qquad (3\text{-}32)$$

Since l here is odd, let $l = 2S + 1$, where S is an integer. Then

$$\frac{l}{2}+1 \to S+\tfrac{3}{2}, \qquad \frac{l}{2}-1 \to S-\tfrac{1}{2}, \qquad \text{and}\quad \sin(S+\tfrac{3}{2})\pi$$

$$= \sin(S-\tfrac{1}{2})\pi = (-1)^{S-1}$$

Utilizing this, we find

$$I_s = \frac{L}{2\pi}\frac{8(-1)^S}{4S^2+4S-3} = \frac{L}{\sqrt{2}}\,{}_2c_{2S+1} \qquad (3\text{-}33)$$

TABLE 3-2 EXPANSION COEFFICIENTS

l	$_2c_l$	$[_2c_l \, _2c_l^*] = _2c_l{}^2$
1	$-\dfrac{\sqrt{2}}{2\pi}\dfrac{8}{3} = -\dfrac{4\sqrt{2}}{3\pi}$	$\dfrac{32}{(9\pi^2)} = .356$
3	$-\dfrac{\sqrt{2}}{2\pi}\dfrac{8}{5} = -\dfrac{4\sqrt{2}}{5\pi}$	$\dfrac{32}{(25\pi^2)} = .128$
5	$\dfrac{\sqrt{2}}{2\pi}\dfrac{8}{21} = \dfrac{4\sqrt{2}}{21\pi}$	$\dfrac{32}{(441\pi^2)} = .007$
7	$-\dfrac{4\sqrt{2}}{45\pi}$	$\dfrac{32}{(2025\pi^2)} = .001$
2	$\dfrac{\sqrt{2}}{2}$	$.50$
$2S, S \neq 1$	0	0

Note: The sum of $_2c_l{}^2 \equiv 1$ (.992 using crude figures).

The particle will thus have a complicated state function after time $t = 0$. Each of these terms will have a time dependent phase which will have a "rotation" rate dependent on the eigenvalue of energy.

What about the energy? The energy before the exchange was

$$_1E_1 = V_0 + \frac{\hbar^2\pi^2}{2mL^2} \ (= V_0 + U_0) \tag{3-34}$$

The energy in any given final state is

$$_2E_n = V_0 + \frac{\hbar^2\pi^2}{8mL^2} n^2 \left(= V_0 + \frac{n^2}{4} U_0 \right) \tag{3-35}$$

These are clearly not the same except for $n = 2$.

If many electrons are involved, each initially in condition *one* with energy $_1E_1$, then we would *measure* only the change of *all* electron energy, which may be found by our probability methods. The values of $_2c_l{}^2$ are thus involved. It is seen that the energy may drop. Indeed $_2c_1{}^2 = .356$ is the probability of a lower energy than the initial value, in fact only one-fourth as much. Now $_2c_2{}^2 = .500$, that is, one-half the time the energy will be unchanged. The rest of the time the energy will be greater than the initial energy. It can be shown that the *average* energy will be unchanged by using the mean value theorem. The values of change times their probabilities should check to this balance if done accurately. The energy change must always be associated with the external mechanism which altered the physical system—in this case the external mechanism that moved the potential wall.

METALS: THE FREE ELECTRON MODEL

In order to get a rough idea of the situation in a metal we assume that those electrons involved in conduction processes are free of the influence of local electric fields of atomic origin; however, there are strong forces keeping them inside the metal. Electric fields are the result of potential gradients. Thus in this case the potential is assumed essentially constant inside the material but the potential becomes very large at the surface of the metal thereby holding the electrons inside. We note that the assumed situation for the metal's electrons is much more closely obeyed by neutral gas molecules enclosed in a box. Indeed we will find that many of our conclusions fit the physical situation for a gas better than for the electrons of a metal. We will consider the possible states of one particle at a time. In the case of electrons we assume that the interactions average out and probably help neutralize the effects of the nuclei. A collision transfers the particle from one eigenfunction to another. The result is that eigenfunctions have only a *probability* of being occupied. This is discussed later.

In considering this problem we first assume that an electron (or gas molecule) can be represented by a state function and that the potential is everywhere zero inside the metal (or box). For simplicity we assume a cubic system. Let the cube edge length be L with the origin at one corner. Then

$$V = 0 \qquad \begin{cases} 0 < x < L \\ 0 < y < L \\ 0 < z < L \end{cases} \qquad \text{(3-36a)}$$

and, for further simplicity,

$$V \to \infty \qquad \begin{cases} x > L & \text{or} & x < 0 \\ y > L & \text{or} & y < 0 \\ z > L & \text{or} & z < 0 \end{cases} \qquad \text{(3-36b)}$$

The Schrödinger equation within the metal is then

$$-\frac{\hbar^2}{2m}\left[\frac{\partial^2}{\partial x^2} + \frac{\partial^2}{\partial y^2} + \frac{\partial^2}{\partial z^2}\right]\psi = -\frac{\hbar}{i}\frac{\partial}{\partial t}\psi \qquad \text{(3-37)}$$

A trial solution taken inside the metal only is of the form

$$\psi = TXYZ \qquad (3\text{-}38)$$

where:

T is a function of t only
X is a function of x only
Y is a function of y only
Z is a function of z only

This solution will be shown to be separable, that is, every variable is expressible in terms of independent factors. The Schrödinger equation becomes

$$-\frac{\hbar^2}{2m}\left[TYZ\frac{d^2X}{dx^2} + TXZ\frac{d^2Y}{dy^2} + TXY\frac{d^2Z}{dz^2}\right] = -\frac{\hbar}{i}XYZ\frac{dT}{dt} \qquad (3\text{-}39)$$

Total derivatives are used as each function is a function of only one variable. Divide by $TXYZ$:

$$-\frac{\hbar^2}{2m}\left[\frac{1}{X}\frac{d^2X}{dx^2} + \frac{1}{Y}\frac{d^2Y}{dy^2} + \frac{1}{Z}\frac{d^2Z}{dz^2}\right] = -\frac{\hbar}{i}\frac{1}{T}\frac{dT}{dt} \qquad (3\text{-}40)$$

Note that the right side of the equation is a function of t only, whereas the left side is not a function of t at all. This is possible under the condition that the two sides equal some constant, which we designate E. Thus

$$-\frac{\hbar}{i}\frac{dT}{dt} = ET \qquad (3\text{-}41)$$

from which

$$T = e^{-iEt/\hbar} \qquad (3\text{-}42)$$

Note that T has the only time dependence in ψ so that the E is the energy of the particle. This is so because equation (3-41) is an energy operator equation, T, the eigenfunction, and E, the eigenvalue. We also have

$$-\frac{\hbar^2}{2m}\left[\frac{1}{X}\frac{d^2X}{dx^2} + \frac{1}{Y}\frac{d^2Y}{dy^2} + \frac{1}{Z}\frac{d^2Z}{dz^2}\right] = E \qquad (3\text{-}43)$$

This can be rewritten as

$$-\frac{\hbar^2}{2m}\left[\frac{1}{Y}\frac{d^2Y}{dy^2} + \frac{1}{Z}\frac{d^2Z}{dz^2}\right] - E = \frac{\hbar^2}{2m}\frac{1}{X}\frac{d^2X}{dx^2} \qquad (3\text{-}44)$$

By reasoning identical to that used previously, the two sides must equal some constant (as the right side is a function of x alone, whereas the left side is independent of x). Let this constant be M_x. Then

$$\frac{\hbar^2}{2m}\frac{1}{X}\frac{d^2X}{dx^2} = M_x \tag{3-45}$$

A trial solution:

$$X = a_x \sin(b_x x + c_x) \tag{3-46}$$

Putting this in (3-45), we obtain

$$-\frac{\hbar^2}{2m}b_x{}^2 = M_x \tag{3-47}$$

Equation (3-43) was completely symmetrical in x, y, and z. Thus we could have placed either Y or Z on the other side of the equation and proceeded in exactly the way X was treated in equations (3-44) to (3-47).

We would then have

$$-\frac{\hbar^2}{2m}b_y{}^2 = M_y$$

and

$$-\frac{\hbar^2}{2m}b_z{}^2 = M_z \tag{3-48}$$

By putting these results back in equation (3-43) we find

$$-M_x - M_y - M_z = E \tag{3-49}$$

or

$$\frac{\hbar^2}{2m}(b_x{}^2 + b_y{}^2 + b_z{}^2) = E \tag{3-50}$$

Now X, Y, and Z have not yet been fully determined. We have not considered the boundary conditions. Here we find the situation to be identical with that discussed earlier [equation (3-11)]. From the logic there we must now conclude that X must be zero at $x = 0$ and at $x = L$, $Y = 0$ at $y = 0$ and at $y = L$, and $Z = 0$ at $z = 0$ and at $z = L$. Thus we find (see 3-11)

$$c_x = c_y = c_z = 0 \tag{3-51}$$

and

$$b_x = \frac{\pi N_x}{L}, \qquad b_y = \frac{\pi N_y}{L}, \qquad b_z = \frac{\pi N_z}{L} \tag{3-52}$$

where N_x, N_y, and N_z are integers. For every integer the bs can be evaluated and, for each combination of bs a different state function results with energy given by (3-50). Using this we find

$$E = \frac{\hbar^2 \pi^2}{2mL^2} N^2 \qquad (3\text{-}53)$$

where

$$N^2 = N_x{}^2 + N_y{}^2 + N_z{}^2 \qquad (3\text{-}54)$$

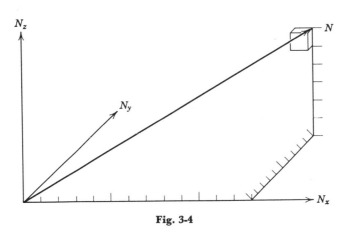

Fig. 3-4

We now would like to see how the states are arranged in energy. It is clear that E depends only on N, and, if we consider a rectangular coordinate system with N_x, N_y, N_z as the ordinates, then N is the radius vector (Fig. 3-4). Note that this is not a "material" space with length dimensions but is a dimensionless space. All possible solutions of the equation are represented by points in this "state space" which are integral numbers of units of each ordinate. There is one such point for each unit of "volume" in the "space." All such points lying inside a sphere of the dimensionless radius N correspond to states having energy less than

$$E = \frac{\pi^2 \hbar^2 N^2}{2mL^2} \qquad (3\text{-}55)$$

A system with 10^{19} electrons, which could be a very small cube having about one millimeter side length, for example, must have a number of states in order to accommodate all the electrons. At $0°K$ those states with energy below some value $E_{\max}$ will be occupied. There must, in fact, be $\frac{1}{2} \times 10^{19}$ points in the state system with energy below $E_{\max}$. This is a very large number and the points are distributed uniformly in our "state space." We can then count points by determining how densely packed they are in state space and multiplying by volume. This means of thinking about the system, and the large densities involved, makes the use of calculus very convenient for accounting. The spherical surface in state space, of radius N, does not pass through many points, but, for the case when N is large, many points lie very close to it. For N large the volume of the sphere approximates the volume of the cubes completely enclosed. Only one octant of the spherical volume subtended by N_n can be considered. Other octants involve substitutions such as $-N_x$ for N_x. This will result in a change of phase only; moreover, this change is arbitrary since it depends on the time factor, T. Thus ψ for $-N_x$ converts to ψ for N_x cyclically. Only positive values of N_x, N_y, and N_z should be considered, others differing only in the arbitrary phase. Hence only one octant of the volume corresponds to spatially different states.

Consider the case of a large number of electrons. According to Pauli's exclusion principle (Postulate VIII), we must have a separate state for each electron. Each spatial eigenfunction of our work up to this time actually corresponds to two different states which differ only in the spin (Postulate VII). Spin is a function of neither time nor position but is a fixed characteristic of the state. Sometimes the eigenfunctions for the two spins are differentiated by including factors s^+ and s^-, which are constants. At absolute zero the electrons will have the lowest possible energies. If the electrons were added to the system one at a time, then the states with lowest energy levels would be filled first. But later electrons would not be able to go into the low energy state and would fill states with the next higher energy. Thus, if there were nL^3 electrons (n is electron density, the number of electrons per unit volume), all states with energy below some energy E_m would be filled, where E_m must be such that there will be nL^3 states with energy equal to or less than E_m. If N_m is the "radius" corresponding to E_m [equation (3-49)], then there must be $L^3n/2$ "integer" points in state space that lie inside the octant of the spherical shell of radius N_m. The factor 2 is due to spin, two electrons share the same spatial function but the states differ in spin.

The "volume" of the octant with N_m as the radius equals the number of possible spatially different states, that is, here the spin is excluded, and this is given by

$$\frac{1}{8}\left(\frac{4}{3}\pi N_m^3\right) \tag{3-56}$$

In order to take care of spin this must equal $L^3n/2$, as explained previously.

Thus

$$N_m{}^3 = \frac{3nL^3}{\pi} \tag{3-57}$$

From (3-55),

$$E_m = \frac{\pi^2 \hbar^2}{2m} \left(\frac{3n}{\pi}\right)^{2/3} \tag{3-58}$$

Thus the energy E_m, the maximum energy of any of these electrons at 0°K, is dependent only on electron *density*. The most energetic state required by electrons at 0°K is seen to have an energy dependent only on the *density* of electrons. The larger the density, the greater the difference in energy between the most energetic and least energetic states. Since this is true, it must also be true that more states are available in a given energy range for larger volumes of material. That is, if the volume is larger and the density is the same, more electrons must be in states in the range $E_m > E > 0$. The number of states available below any selected energy must therefore be proportional to the volume involved, and this can be checked.

Examine equations (3-52) and (3-50). Consider the system where the energy maximum and electron density are kept constant but the volume is multiplied by 8 by doubling L. Then the maximum values of the Ns can be doubled and the sphere of radius N in state space will be twice as large without exceeding the limits imposed on the bs by (3-50). Thus the *volume* in state space will also go up by a factor of eight. It is therefore proper to speak of numbers of states per unit volume. As will be seen later, however, this is *not* what is known as the *density of states*. The electron density is then related to the maximum energy by

$$n = \frac{1}{3\pi^2} \left(\frac{\sqrt{2mE_m}}{\hbar}\right)^3 \tag{3-59}$$

Note that only electron *density* is involved and not the total number of electrons. An increase of E_m by dE_m increases the number of states per unit volume by

$$dn = \frac{m\sqrt{2mE_m}}{\pi^2 \hbar^3} dE_m \tag{3-60}$$

The *density of states* (in energy), defined as the number of states per unit volume per unit energy in the neighborhood of a given energy E, is proportional to $E^{1/2}$. Here, as elsewhere, density gives an idea of crowding.

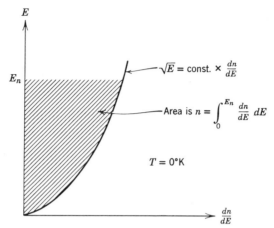

Fig. 3-5   The density of states versus the energy at $T = 0°K$.

The crowding here involves the spacing of states in energy: the number of states per unit energy that are involved (Fig. 3-5).

It is seen that some electrons are very energetic even at low temperatures. No heat energy can be abstracted from them. They cannot lose energy because this would require them to have less energy after the abstraction. This is not possible because no lower energy situations are available to them.

BARRIER PENETRATION

In classical mechanics an object cannot have negative kinetic energy and therefore it cannot be in any region where its total energy is less than its potential energy. Thus an electron that is in an enclosed region completely surrounded by high potential energy space (where an electron would have less total energy than just the potential "component") would be confined to the enclosed region.

In quantum mechanics we find that the wave function of a particle may be nonzero in these "forbidden" regions. If the "forbidden" region is not too thick or too "forbidden," a particle has a reasonable probability of penetrating through the barrier to the other side. It does *not* have to surmount the barrier. Such phenomena are observed in so-called "field emission" where electrons are pulled out of solids by high electric fields, in alpha decay of atom nucleii, in ionization of certain atomic vapors by collision with certain solids, in metal-semiconductor contacts, in tunnel diodes, and probably in numerous other situations. For a simple model the penetration of a barrier can be calculated.

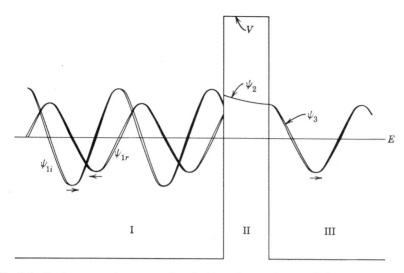

Fig. 3-6 Barrier penetration or tunneling. Incident electrons have too little energy to go over barrier. Real projections of complex momenta eigenfunctions $e^{ipx/\hbar}$ are shown. Visualize ψ_{1i} and ψ_3 as right-hand helices and ψ_{1r} as a left-hand helix.

Assume that a beam of electrons of energy E strikes a barrier of thickness s with a potential $V > E$ for electrons. Figure 3-6 shows the situation. The two regions outside of the barrier, regions I and III, have zero potential energy. The incident beam partially penetrates the barrier, resulting in a transmitted beam in region III; and the barrier partially reflects the beam resulting in a return beam in region I.

Note that in a classical case no possibility of penetration exists. In the quantum mechanical situation a wave function does exist in a region where the total energy is less than the potential energy alone. No classical analog exists. (See legend of Fig. 5-1.)

The incident beam may be characterized by

$$\psi_{1i} = e^{+ipx/\hbar} \tag{3-61}$$

and the reflected beam by

$$\psi_{1r} = e^{-ipx/\hbar} \tag{3-62}$$

No coefficients are shown since the functions cannot be normalized in these regions. The normalization could be done so that $\psi\psi^*$ is proportional to the charge density in the beam (beam current density by beam velocity). It will be so interpreted hereafter.

The state function form appropriate to region I is

$$\psi_1 = a\psi_{1i} + b\psi_{1r} \tag{3-63}$$

The magnitude of the momentum, when an electron is observed in the reflected beam, is the same as in the incident beam. This must be so if (3-63) is a solution to Schrödinger's equation. In other words, the electrons are either reflected elastically or transmitted. Thus the electrons that are transmitted also will have the same momentum (the potential energy being the same). Then

$$\psi_{3t} = e^{+ipx/\hbar} \qquad (3\text{-}64)$$

There is no reflected wave in region III. The state function form appropriate to region III is then $\psi_3 = c\psi_{3t}$. The requirements on the momentum can be easily checked as the state functions in each region must satisfy Schrödinger's equation:

$$\frac{-\hbar^2}{2m} \frac{\partial^2 \psi}{\partial x^2} = E\psi \qquad (3\text{-}65)$$

With any of the preceding forms $E = p^2/2m$. The probability of reflection is just

$$\frac{bb^*}{aa^*}$$

which are the probabilities associated with observing electrons in the reflected and incident wave respectively. Similarly the transmission coefficient must be

$$\frac{cc^*}{aa^*}$$

At the boundaries ($x = \pm s/2$) both ψ and $\partial\psi/\partial x$ must be continuous. (The latter continuity condition is required as the discontinuity in V is not infinite.) Let

$$\psi_2 = fe^{+\alpha x} + ge^{-\alpha x} \qquad (3\text{-}66)$$

Then, to satisfy Schrödinger's equation,

$$\frac{-\hbar^2}{2m}\alpha^2 + V = E \qquad (3\text{-}67)$$

$$\alpha = \frac{1}{\hbar}\sqrt{2m(V-E)} \qquad (3\text{-}68)$$

Since V is greater than E in this region, α is real and can be either positive or negative. If it is positive, then the term with f as a coefficient would grow as x increases, whereas the term with g as coefficient would be attenuated. Attenuation will dominate. (See f/g below.)

The equations for the four boundary conditions are

$$ae^{-ips/2\hbar} + be^{ips/2\hbar} \qquad -fe^{-\alpha s/2} \quad -ge^{\alpha s/2} \qquad = 0$$

$$ae^{-ips/2\hbar} - be^{ips/2\hbar} \qquad -\frac{\alpha\hbar}{ip}fe^{-\alpha s/2} + \frac{\alpha\hbar}{ip}ge^{\alpha s/2} = 0$$

$$-ce^{ips/2\hbar} + \frac{\alpha\hbar}{ip}fe^{\alpha s/2} - \frac{\alpha\hbar}{ip}ge^{-\alpha s/2} = 0 \qquad (3\text{-}69)$$

$$-ce^{ips/2\hbar} + fe^{\alpha s/2} \qquad +ge^{-\alpha s/2} \qquad = 0$$

From this we find

$$\frac{b}{a} = \frac{2}{\Delta}\left(1 + \frac{\alpha^2\hbar^2}{p^2}\right)\sinh 2\alpha s \qquad (3\text{-}70a)$$

$$\frac{c}{a} = -\frac{4}{\Delta}\left(\frac{\alpha\hbar}{ip}\right) \qquad (3\text{-}70b)$$

$$\Delta = 2e^{ips/\hbar}\left\{\frac{2\alpha\hbar}{ip}\cosh 2\alpha s - \left(1 - \frac{\alpha^2\hbar^2}{p^2}\right)\sinh 2\alpha s\right\} \qquad (3\text{-}70c)$$

$$\frac{bb^*}{aa^*} = \frac{4}{\Delta\Delta^*}\left(1 + \frac{\alpha^2\hbar^2}{p^2}\right)^2\sinh^2 2\alpha s \qquad (3\text{-}70d)$$

$$\frac{cc^*}{aa^*} = \frac{16}{\Delta\Delta^*}\frac{\alpha^2\hbar^2}{p^2} \qquad (3\text{-}70e)$$

$$\frac{f}{g} = e^{-\alpha s}\frac{\alpha\hbar + ip}{\alpha\hbar - ip} \qquad (3\text{-}70f)$$

The magnitude of $\Delta\Delta^*$ goes up exponentially for large αs and this causes the penetration cc^*/aa^* to drop off very rapidly.

A more careful analysis of barrier penetration must involve transitions such as those discussed in Chapter VIII. The eigenfunctions appropriate to the two sides of the barrier are generally very different rather than the same, as was assumed here. Nevertheless, the kind of calculation done here is very informative and is normally used in modified form in situations where more precise calculations are too difficult (see Chapter VIII).

PROBLEMS

1. A potential well, or box, exists such that in the regions I, where $x < -L/2$, and III, where $x > L/2$, $V = V_1$. In the region II, where $-L/2 < x < L/2$, $V = V_0 < V_1$. $\psi_\text{I}, \psi_\text{II}$, and ψ_III are the analytic expressions suitable in regions I, II, and III, respectively.

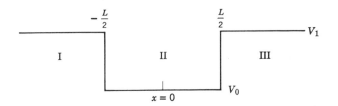

(a) What are the relationships between

$$\frac{\partial\psi_{\mathrm{I}}}{\partial x}, \quad \frac{\partial\psi_{\mathrm{II}}}{\partial x}, \quad \frac{\partial\psi_{\mathrm{III}}}{\partial x}, \quad \psi_{\mathrm{I}}, \quad \psi_{\mathrm{II}}, \quad \psi_{\mathrm{III}}$$

at $x = -L/2$ and at $x = L/2$?
Consider a solution for Schrödinger's equation such that $E < V_1$.

(b) Must we have $E > V_0$?

(c) What can be said about the *signs* of

$$\frac{1}{\psi}\frac{\partial^2\psi}{\partial x^2}$$

in regions I, II, III, respectively? How are the directions of curvature related to the axis?

2. (a) Express the state function $_2\psi$ of the transition example of the text in terms of the $_2\psi_n$s [equation (3-24)].

(b) Using the mean value theorem, express the average measured energy for $_2\psi$.

3. For the transition example of the text *plot* the state function at $t = -\epsilon$, where it is represented by $_1\psi$, where ϵ is arbitrarily small. Plot, on the same coordinates, the state function at $t = +\hbar/(V_0 + 50U_0)$, where it is represented by $_2\psi$.

4. Why does very rapid motion of the wall represented by the states $_1\psi$ and $_2\psi$ of equations (3-23) and (3-24) require infinite energy as stated in the text, if the continuity of form versus time is discontinuous?

5. How does $_1\psi_1$ differ from $_2\psi_2$? Since the state function is not a physically measurable quantity and since these two have the same eigenvalue of energy, is there physical meaning in the difference?

6. At 0°K what is the total energy of all electrons in a cubic box of sides L in terms of the number of electrons? What is the average energy of the electrons in terms of the energy of the most energetic electron?

7. Consider the case of the free electron metal of cubic form, sides L. A pressure is exerted on the metal so that it is compressed so that the sides are each now $0.99L$. What work was involved? What *pressure* was involved?

8. A region is bounded by $x = 0$, $x = L$, $y = 0$, $y = L$. Electrons are confined to this region. Here ψ is a state function which is zero outside of this region; in the region it has the form

$$\psi = a \exp\left[-iE_{r,n} \frac{t}{\hbar} \right] \sin \frac{r\pi x}{L} \sin \frac{n\pi y}{L}$$

Here a, r, and n are constants; r and n are also real.

(**a**) Can r and n have any integral values except zero? Can they have any noninteger values? *Explain.*

(**b**) What is the basis of the statement that

$$aa^* \int_0^L \int_0^L \sin^2 \frac{r\pi x}{L} \sin^2 \frac{n\pi y}{L} \ dx \, dy = 1$$

Explain each limit and each differential. Why is no time function involved? Evaluate aa^*. Why can neither r nor n be zero?

(**c**) (i) What values may $E_{r,n}$ have? How many *electron* states for an r n pair?

(ii) Plot all of the positive values of r and n for which $E_{r,n}$ has values *equal to* or *less than* $51\pi^2\hbar^2/mL^2$ on an r versus n coordinate system.

(iii) Plot several "contours" of approximately constant $E_{r,n}$ on the same plot.

9. A region similar to that in Problem 8 is bounded by $x = 0$ and $x = 2L$, $y = 0$ and $y = L$. Twice as much volume is involved. What is the proper form for ψ? Repeat all parts of Problem 8 for this case. How many electrons (remembering two spins), *per unit area*, have energy less than $51\pi^2\hbar^2/mL^2$? How does *this* compare with square case of Problem 8?

10. Show that in the barrier penetration example in the text [equation (3-70)],

$$aa^* = bb^* + cc^*$$

Also show, for the case $\alpha = ip/\hbar$ and $V = 0$, that $bb^* = 0$. Explain both of these and their significance in physical terms.

11. It can be shown by the principle of conservation of charge and by use of Schrödinger's equation that the electron current density is given by

$$\mathbf{J} = -\frac{\hbar q}{2mi} (\psi \, \nabla\psi^* - \psi^* \, \nabla\psi)$$

Show, in the text's barrier penetration example, that $\mathbf{J}$ is independent of position or time. Note that the momentum operation is involved, with a coefficient q/m to convert to current density.

IV

STATISTICS

In discussing the free electron model for a metal we mentioned that the model was even more appropriate when applied to the molecules of a gas. The difference between the models for a gas, for a semiconductor, and for a metal lie largely in the way the electrons or molecules fill (or occupy) the states involved. It was shown how electrons at the absolute zero of temperature behaved. The energy that is added to the system to raise it above absolute zero goes partly into electron energy (in the free electron model) or into the kinetic energy of the gas molecules (in a gas, of course). The energy separation of eigenfunctions is very much less for heavy particles and this makes a great difference in the interaction of particles at higher temperatures. The occupancy problems—the conditions involved in determining which state function describes a particle—differ greatly between electrons and molecules. This difference accounts for almost everything other than the electron charge. The charge is essential to the conduction process and it also enters the potential function in the determination of the Hamiltonian.

FERMI-DIRAC STATISTICS

The electrons at absolute zero of temperature all lie in the lowest possible states, one electron to a state. (Two states which differ only in their spin are separate states.) Because all of the lowest energy states are occupied, no energy can be removed from this system even though some of the electrons have considerable kinetic energy. In fact, the meaning of absolute zero of temperature lies in the inability to remove energy of a kinetic nature. At other than absolute zero temperature there is some removable energy. We can add energy to a solid and it will get hot; not all electrons are then in their lowest possible energy states. How are the electrons distributed among the states to achieve the higher total energy?

In asking this question we have implicitly made two critical assumptions: first, that a distribution exists; second, that the electron energy is the important difference between states as far as this assumed distribution is concerned. We formalize these by explicitly assuming, *first*, that a distribution does exist and, *second*, that all states are equally likely to be occupied by an electron except for energy considerations. Let the probability of the ith state being occupied be f_i where, according to our assumption, f_i is only a function of the ith state's energy.

Consider a system of many electrons that have been isolated in all ways for a long time. It has then, by definition, come to "equilibrium." The system has a fixed amount of energy and a large number of quantum states that are clearly separated in energy—there may, in fact, exist large spans of energy which correspond to no states. Such spans are called *energy gaps*.

In the isolated system the electrons may be involved in transitions from one state to another (or "jump" from one state to another), providing, among other things, that energy and momentum are conserved. In order to combine such limitations with the jumping process we consider two electrons that interact in such a way that both will make transitions. For example, a collision could take place between these two particles, in which case momentum and energy will be conserved. In fact, only by interactions involving several entities can we have these satisfy basic conservation laws which are part of quantum mechanics.

In the quantum mechanics involving transitions the sense of direction of time is lost. Physically this means that reactions are equally likely to take place forward or backward in time. In considering time we note first that in quantum mechanics it arises only when energy is involved. Therefore the Schrödinger equation is a natural place to look at the "nature" of time. One can get some feeling for this by substituting $-t_2$ for t_1 in Schrödinger's equation:

$$\hat{H}\psi = -\frac{\hbar}{i}\frac{\partial\psi}{\partial t_1} = \frac{\hbar}{i}\frac{\partial\psi}{\partial t_2}$$

Compare this with the complex conjugate equation,

$$\hat{H}^*\psi = \frac{\hbar}{i}\frac{\partial\psi}{\partial t_1}$$

remembering that, in the systems we have discussed, $\hat{H}$ is real, and therefore

$\hat{H}^* = \hat{H}$. It is clear that the time reversal equation is identical with the complex conjugate equation, which in turn has identical physical meaning with the starting equation. Thus we can state that quantum mechanical factors do not cause us to prefer one direction for the " flow of time." Hence the same quantum mechanical factors are involved in a process and in its inverse.

We make a third assumption, the so-called *principle of detailed balancing*: In thermal equilibrium every identifiable physical process proceeds *on the average* at exactly the same rate as its own inverse. One physical process cannot be compensated for by a different one; each must *self-balance* independently of the others.

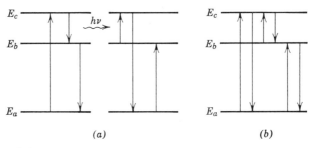

(a)   *(b)*

Fig. 4-1 Detailed Balancing and Perpetual Motion. (a) The system on the left makes transitions predominantly in the sequences $a \rightarrow c \rightarrow b \rightarrow a$. It emits a photon of radiation $h\nu$ of energy $E_c - E_b$. The system in the right absorbes the photon making the transition $b \rightarrow c \rightarrow a \rightarrow b$. Other transitions are not photon coupled in this system. Therefore energy flows to the right with no temperature difference. (b) A system with detailed balancing.

The principle of detailed balancing can be put on an intuitively acceptable basis by the following considerations. Figure 4-1 shows some energy values, labeled E_a, E_b, and E_c, for some eigenfunctions. The system for which these are energy eigenvalues is considered to be in equilibrium. Thus a single temperature is involved. The arrows indicate the direction of transitions as an electron changes from one eigenfunction to another. The energy received by (or given up by) the electron comes from (or goes to) other electrons, for example. Thus this diagram indicates that an interaction is taking place. The $a \rightarrow c$ transfer indicates that the electron has received some energy, where the $c \rightarrow b$ transfer indicates that it has given up some, possibly in the form of a quantum of radiation, a photon.

If the transitions went only in the direction shown in Fig. 4-1a, a clever person might be able to develop useful power from it by absorbing photons of a given energy, even with an absorber at the same temperature. This is so because, without the requirement of detailed balance, the absorber is not required to return equal quantities of the same energy photons. Thus the absorber could get hot and the system of Fig. 4-1 could get cold—all without an external energy source. The temperature difference that could thus be developed could drive a heat engine. This abstraction of power would be contrary to the second law of thermodynamics, and if it were possible, perpetual motion would be possible. It is therefore not possible and transitions must take place with equal frequency in either direction as shown in Fig. 4-1b.

Let us now examine a system of four states such that the energy eigenvalues are related by

$$E_1 - E_2 = E_3 - E_4 \qquad (4\text{-}1)$$

If we assume that an electron goes from state one to state two and an interacting electron goes from state four to state three simultaneously, we will at least have a conservation of energy (Fig. 4-2). Making use of our various assumptions, we can examine the probability of occurrence of this reaction.

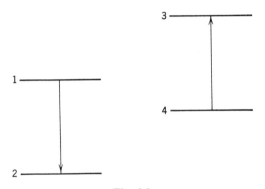

Fig. 4-2

This reaction can take place only if states one and four are initially occupied; thus the probability of occurrence of the reaction must have this $f_1 \times f_4$ as a factor. Moreover, due to the Pauli exclusion principle, states two and three must be initially unoccupied in order for the reaction to proceed. The probability for the unoccupancy of both is $(1 - f_2) \times (1 - f_3)$. Furthermore, a quantum mechanical electronic interaction factor must be included —simply given as F here. Thus the probability of the interaction taking place is

$$f_1 f_4 (1 - f_2)(1 - f_3) F = P \qquad (4\text{-}2)$$

The *principle of detailed balancing* requires that the inverse process take place with equal likelihood. In the inverse process the electrons must start in states two and three and finish in states one and four. Thus

$$f_2 f_3 (1 - f_1)(1 - f_4) F = P \tag{4-3}$$

the quantum mechanical term being unchanged.

Then we must have

$$f_1 f_4 (1 - f_2)(1 - f_3) = f_2 f_3 (1 - f_1)(1 - f_4) \tag{4-4}$$

Dividing by $f_2 f_4 (1 - f_1)(1 - f_3)$ yields

$$\frac{f_1}{1 - f_1} \frac{1 - f_2}{f_2} = \frac{f_3}{1 - f_3} \frac{1 - f_4}{f_4} \tag{4-5}$$

Note that the left side is a function of E_1 and E_2 only and the right side is a function of E_3 and E_4 only. Since the two sides are equal and are related only because of equal energy differences, as stated in equation (4-1), each side in itself must be a function of the energy difference only. That is,

$$\frac{f_1}{1 - f_1} \frac{1 - f_2}{f_2} \tag{4-6}$$

is a function of the energy difference $(E_1 - E_2)$ only. The energies are involved as a difference. To put the probability factors in a compatible difference form too, clearly a logarithmic expression is needed. Let

$$G_1 = \ln \frac{f_1}{1 - f_1} \quad \text{and} \quad G_2 = \ln \frac{f_2}{1 - f_2} \tag{4-7}$$

Since the fs are functions of energy only, G_1 is a function of E_1 only and G_2 is a function of E_2 only, while from the statement (4-6) we find $G_1 - G_2$ is a function of $E_1 - E_2$ only.

Let us consider states dE_1 above E_1 and dE_2 above E_2. If $dE_1 = dE_2$, then $E_1 - E_2$ is unchanged and then $G_1 - G_2$ must also be unchanged. Thus $dG_1 = dG_2$. Let

$$\frac{dG_1}{dE_1} = -L_1, \qquad \frac{dG_2}{dE_2} = -L_2 \tag{4-8}$$

Then

$$0 = dG_1 - dG_2 = -L_1 \, dE_1 + L_2 \, dE_2 = (L_2 - L_1) \, dE_1 \tag{4-9}$$

from which

$$L_1 = L_2 \tag{4-10}$$

Thus, since the energies were arbitrarily chosen, L must be independent of energy. We then have an equation of G_1:

$$\int_{G_F}^{G_1} dG = -L \int_{E_F}^{E_1} dE \tag{4-11}$$

Let us take as a reference energy E_F, that value for which $G_F = 0$. This is, according to our definition, the energy for which f, the probability of occupancy, is one-half. The subscript F is chosen because this energy is called the Fermi level of energy. Then

$$G_1 = -L(E_1 - E_F) = L(E_F - E_1) \tag{4-12}$$

From the definition of G_1,

$$\ln \frac{f_1}{1 - f_1} = L(E_F - E_1) \tag{4-13}$$

or

$$\frac{1}{f_1} - 1 = \exp - L(E_F - E_1) \tag{4-14}$$

which can be put in the more usual form

$$f_1 = \frac{1}{1 + \exp L(E_1 - E_F)} \tag{4-15}$$

Note that for $E_1 = E_F$ the exponential equals unity and $f_1 = \frac{1}{2}$ as required by our choice of $G_F = 0$. For $E_1 \gg E_F$ the exponential is very large compared to unity and $f_1 = \exp - L(E_1 - E_F)$. It is clear that in this case f_1 is small, and, in equation (4-14), we could have neglected the one in comparison with f_1^{-1}. We would then have obtained the same exponential dependence, of course.

Occupancy equation (4-15) is used to calculate total energy. The total electronic energy of the isolated system is the sum of the energies of all electrons. The states have certain energies and probabilities of occupation associated with them. The total energy is then

$$U_t = \sum_i E_i f_i = \sum_{\substack{\text{all} \\ \text{states}}} E_i \frac{1}{1 + \exp L(E_i - E_F)} \tag{4-16}$$

One can compute dU_T/dL and find the variation of the total energy with the variable L. On comparison with experiment, L is identified with $(kT)^{-1}$. With this identification, equation (4-15) becomes

$$f_1 = \frac{1}{1 + \exp(E_1 - E_F)/kT} \tag{4-17}$$

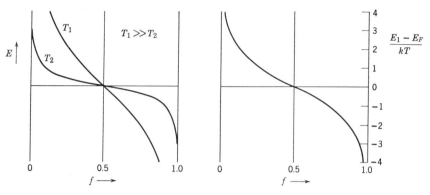

Fig. 4-3

This relationship, known as the Fermi-Dirac distribution function, is plotted in Fig. 4-3.

Figure 4-3 indicates that a point of symmetry exists. The probability of a state having energy E_1 being empty (or being occupied by a "hole") is $1 - f_1 = f_{h1}$ where f_1 is a function of $E_1 - E_F$. We will show that f_{h1} is the same function as f_1 but with the energy reversed in sign, namely, $f_{h1} = f_1(E_F - E_1)$. Using $\beta_1 \equiv (E_1 - E_F)kT$, we have

$$f_1 = (1 + e^{\beta_1})^{-1}$$

Thus

$$f_{h1} = 1 - f_1 = 1 - \frac{1}{1 + e^{\beta_1}} = \frac{1 + e^{\beta_1} - 1}{1 + e^{\beta_1}} = \frac{e^{\beta_1}}{1 + e^{\beta_1}}$$

and

$$f_{h1} = \frac{1}{e^{-\beta_1} + 1} = (1 + e^{-\beta_1})^{-1}$$

Q.E.D.

We see that statistically, at least, the empty states below E_F have the same characteristics of the filled states above E_F with a reversal of the sense of energy. This symmetry proves very valuable when dealing with the concept of holes in semiconductors.

THE FERMI LEVEL

The Fermi level itself has some very important uses and implications. To get a better feel for it let us consider a system such as in Fig. 4-4a, which

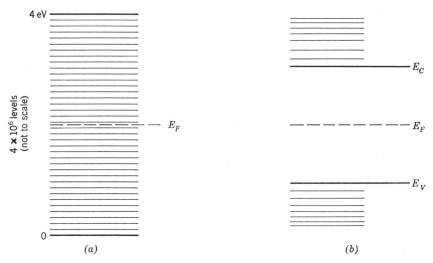

Fig. 4-4 The difference $E - E_F$ always appears in statistics since the artibrary zero of energy must drop out. Here the levels are equally spaced in (a).

shows a band of equally spaced levels. To be specific, let the levels be 1 μeV (10^{-6} eV) apart and the band be 4 eV from bottom to top. Then there are 4×10^6 levels or 8×10^6 states in the band. If there were 4×10^6 electrons in the band, and the temperature were 0°K, the lowest energy half of the states would be filled and the highest energy half would be empty.

The Fermi level must be at such a position to agree with this situation. At 0°K the Fermi factor, f, must be zero for $E > E_F$ and unity for $E < E_F$. In this case then, each state above E_F is certain to be empty, whereas each below E_F is certain to be filled. Then E_F will be just above the highest filled level and just below the lowest empty level. This fixes E_F precisely, even at 0°K, since the energy levels are so close together. There are 2×10^6 levels of filled states and 2×10^6 so-called empty levels. (Note: The "level" terminology is used, but it is the states that are filled or empty, not the levels per se.) Thus E_F must be at 2×10^6 (occupied levels) $\times 10^{-6}$ (eV per level) $= 2.0$ eV above the bottom of the band.

Suppose the temperature is raised somewhat above 0°K. The number of states filled must still be 4×10^6 since raising the temperature neither creates nor destroys electrons. Some of the previously filled levels will be empty and some of the previously empty levels will be filled. In raising the temperature we make some of the electrons more energetic, moving them from lower energy states to higher energy states.

We have selected a symmetric situation where there are as many unfilled as filled states. We now look at the statistics. The probability of a state at $\epsilon + E_B$ being filled is

$$f(\epsilon + E_B) = \frac{1}{1 + \exp(\epsilon + E_B - E_F)/kT}$$

Here E_B is the bottom state of the band and ϵ is some arbitrary energy. This must be just the same as the probability of a state ϵ (same arbitrary energy) from the top of the band (i.e., at energy $E_T - \epsilon$) being empty. But this has been given as

$$1 - f(E_T - \epsilon) = f_h(E_T - \epsilon) = \frac{1}{1 + \exp(E_F - E_T + \epsilon)/kT}$$

Since

$$f(\epsilon + E_B) = f_h(E_T - \epsilon)$$

and the two forms are identical, the two exponentials must be equal:

$$\frac{\epsilon + E_B - E_F}{kT} = \frac{E_F - E_T + \epsilon}{kT}$$

The ϵ/kT can be subtracted from each side to give

$$E_F = \frac{E_B + E_T}{2}$$

Thus E_F is in the center of the band independent of temperature. The E_F does not change with temperature when symmetrically situated as the Fermi function itself is symmetrical between filled and empty states.

Now let us examine Fig. 4-4b. Here the system is again symmetric but we note that the Fermi level is now situated between two bands of states and is itself in a region where there are no states. Enough electrons are present to fill the lower band of states at 0°K but no extra electrons are involved to fill any states of the upper band.

As the temperature is raised an electron must take on a large amount of energy if it takes on any. That is, small amounts of extra energy would not be enough to permit them to be in any of the available states. Since large amounts of energy will not be available at low temperatures the electrons will not contribute to the specific heat at low temperatures. Electrons will remain in the lowest levels; thus no empty states will result in the lower band and no "free" electrons in the upper band.

Because of the symmetry between the two bands and the symmetry of the Fermi function, the eventual production of "holes" (empty states in the lower band) and "electrons" (electrons in the upper band) will take place at elevated temperature in a symmetric way. The Fermi level itself will remain in the center of the so-called " gap."

The magnitude of $E - E_F$ will be large compared to kT for E applicable to any of the possible states. Thus $\exp(E - E_F)/kT$, for energies of the upper band levels, or $\exp(E_F - E)/kT$, for energies of the lower band levels, will always be large compared to one. The Fermi statistics may be simplified.

BOLTZMANN STATISTICS

To get some idea of magnitudes, kT for room temperature is about $1/40$ eV of energy. The factor kT is involved everywhere in statistics. Since it has dimensions of energy and since electron volts are used so much in this field, it becomes convenient to think of k in terms of eV/deg: $k = (11,600^{-1}$ eV/deg. Thus the exponential becomes very large if $E - E_F > 0.1$ eV (i.e., $\beta > 4$). In this case the *one* in the denominator can be neglected in its additive effect and the expression for f becomes simply

$$f = e^{-\beta} \tag{4-19}$$

This is known as Boltzmann's distribution (or statistics). When $E_F - E > 0.1$ eV (note the change in sign), $-\beta > 4$, and, from equation (4-18), we see that

$$f_h = e^{\beta} \tag{4-20}$$

This is a form of Boltzmann's statistics suitable for holes. The Boltzmann forms are useful whenever the electrons or holes are dilute and therefore have only minor interaction. In fact *dilute* in this sense *means* that many possible states for these " particles " are unoccupied, that is, that f, or f_h, is small. The only way these probability factors can be small is for the Fermi statistics' exponentials to be large in comparison to unity. Thus in the dilute case, Fermi statistics reduces to Boltzmann statistics.

Consider again the energy values of equation (3-21):

$$E_k = V_0 + \frac{\hbar^2}{2m}\left(\frac{k\pi}{L}\right)^2$$

where k took on integral values. (Note that this k is *not* Boltzmann's constant.) In particular consider the spacings of energy values for (a) the case of an electron and (b) the case of a molecule of oxygen. The mass of the oxygen molecule is $32 \times 1845 = 5.9 \times 10^4$ larger than that of the electron. Thus, when $k = 10$ for an electron the energy will be the same as for $k = 2430$ for an oxygen molecule. There will therefore be many hundreds of times as many levels in a given energy range for oxygen as there will be for the electrons. One result is that, for a given nonzero temperature, even low energy levels may be unfilled in the oxygen molecule case simply because there are too many levels for the molecules to fill. Thus they have a large probability of being empty, just the situation needed to produce Boltzmann statistics. (Actually oxygen does not obey Fermi statistics even in the very low temperature state; it obeys the so-called Einstein-Bose statistics, however, and not Boltzmann's. The Einstein-Bose statistics has a *form* somewhat like that of Fermi statistics, and it reduces to Boltzmann statistics in a similar manner.)

JUNCTIONS AND INTERFACES

In the derivation of Fermi statistics, no limit was placed on the spatial distribution of the electronic states. It was explicitly assumed that only energy considerations were involved in the problem of occupancy. No exceptions were made relative to spatial configurations. As a result the conclusions are equally valid for *any* spatial distribution. Consider, then, the situation shown in Fig. 4-5 where two materials come together and have a common interface. (A metal and a semiconductor, two types of semi-

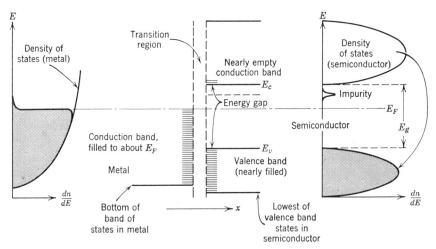

Fig. 4-5 Metal-semiconductor interface. A metal and a semiconductor are in contact and have a common Fermi level. The center portion of the figure shows a usual so-called energy level diagram. E_c and E_v are lowest and highest energies associated with the conduction bands and valence bands respectively. E_F is the same for metal and semiconductor. No energy level need be even near the Fermi level in the semiconductor. Some donors are shown as in *n*-type material. On the left, the density of states is shown for the "ideal" metal. Its levels are filled to the region of the Fermi level. The density of states for a semiconductor (on right) has two major regions. These lobes may be moved up or down *together* (relative to E_F) by choice and amount of impurity.

conductors, an oxide "protective" layer over a metal, all are of this form.)
The electronic states in one material do not have the same form as that in the
other material but, since the electrons can interact, the statistics are treated
just as though only one system exists. One primary result is that only one
Fermi level (E_F) of energy exists.

The system can of course be thought of as consisting of two component
systems, each with its own states and eigenfunctions. In each system the
occupation of the states is given by the Fermi-Dirac distribution function.
The two systems, which are in equilibrium with each other, have the same
Fermi level.

Although we will not prove it here, the Fermi level is identical to the
chemical potential for electrons. (Some scientists call this the electro-
chemical potential.) When two systems are in equilibrium it is the chemical
potential that has no gradient and therefore no chemical driving force
exists.

As an example of the use of Fermi-Dirac statistics let us examine the
density of states plot (Fig. 3-5) in Fig. 4-6.

Note that as the temperature goes up, some electronic states of higher
energy are filled by electrons that have moved from lower energy states. Of
course these plots are of probabilities and indicate the fraction of time

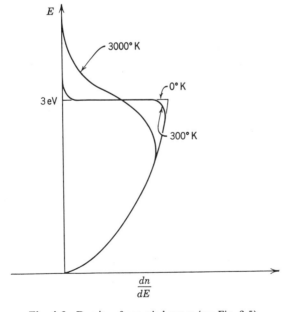

Fig. 4-6 Density of occupied states (see Fig. 3-5).

occupied rather than that specific states are filled or empty. Because of the large numbers involved, however, they also represent the proportion of states which are filled in any particular energy range. As a result some energy has gone into the electronic system as the temperature goes up. This gives rise to the heat capacity of the electrons. Most electrons do not change their energy even at high temperature, so clearly not all of them are contributing to the heat capacity. The explanation of the observed low heat capacity of metals was an early success of quantum mechanics.

PROBLEMS

1. A system has state functions such that the eigenvalues of energy are given as $E_n = (n + 1/2)g$ where the ns are integers. (This is the energy system appropriate to a simple harmonic oscillator.) Here $g = 0.01$ eV. For each level of energy two states exist, one for each of two spins.
   (a) Find the Fermi level, E_F, when the system has 91 electrons and the system is at a temperature such that $kT = 0.025$ eV. Show your work.
   (b) What is the temperature in °F?
   (c) How much does the Fermi level change when another electron is added and what energy increase does the system have by this addition?

2. Construct the energy level diagram appropriate to two silicon regions in contact, one of p-type and one of n-type. (Compare with Fig. 4-4.) The highest energy in the valence band, called the valence band edge, is designated E_{vn} in the n-type material and E_{vp} in the p-type. In our problem they are related so that $E_{vn} = E_{vp} - 0.2$ eV. The energy gap $(E_c - E_v)$, or E_g, is 1.1 eV and is independent of whether the material is n- or p-type. Assume symmetry of states about the middle of the energy gap in either region, that is, the top of the valence band and the bottom of the conduction band are mirror images in their dn/dE versus E characteristics. (This is not quite true but is adequate for our present purposes.)
   (a) Evalute $E_{cp} - E_{cn}$. What are the maximum and minimum values of $E_F - E_{vn}$?
      How close is the Fermi level to E_{cn}, E_{cp}, E_{vp}?
      (*Hint*: E_F must be sufficiently near E_{cn}, the bottom of the conduction band in the n-type material, for this to be n-type. It must also be sufficiently close to E_{vp} for it to make this material p-type.)
   (b) What change in potential energy would an electron experience in going from a conduction band state in the p-type material to its corresponding state in the n-type material? (Here "corresponding states" means the states having the same energy differences from

the conduction band bottom in their respective materials.) Use words
and be clear.

(c) In making statistical calculations on either of the bands of states,
are Fermi statistics needed or would Boltzmann statistics do?
(Assume 1% accuracy is good.) Express in terms of E_F and E_{cn}:
(i) The fraction of the states occupied in the p-type material in the
energy range near $E_{cp} + 0.4$ eV. (ii) The fraction of the states
occupied in the n-type region where the energy is $E_{cn} + 0.1$ eV.

(d) Express in terms of E_F and E_{cn}: (i) The fraction of states occupied in
the n-type silicon at $E_{cn} + 0.4$ eV. (ii) The fraction of states occupied
in the p-type silicon at $E_{cp} + 0.1$ eV. Compare with (c) and show
the ratio of conduction band states occupied in the n-type to those
occupied in the p-type. Is this ratio dependent on the 0.1 eV and
0.4 eV chosen above or is it general for any energy above the conduction band? What, then, is the ratio of the *number of electrons* per
unit volume in the n-type to the p-type silicon?

3. Consider the hypothetical case of a semiconductor having 0.01 cm³
volume, a band gap $E_g = 0.3$ eV, and the width of the valence and
conduction band each equal to 2 eV as shown in the figure. The pairs of

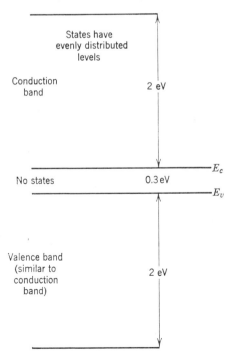

electronic states in the bands are uniformly distributed in energy and in each band they have a spatial density of 10^{21} levels/cm^3. (Note that this is a hypothetical distribution and is unlike those discussed in the text.) The temperature is 292°K. In the calculations to be done do not consider impurity levels (even though impurity atoms may be involved in supplying electrons). Thus only states in the bands as shown may have electrons in this problem.

(a) How widely spaced in energy are the energy levels? Taking spin into account, find the number of electrons required to fill half the valence band states. Show by symmetry that this is independent of temperature except at very high temperatures. Find the number of electrons needed (i) to produce as many electrons in the conduction band as holes in the valence band and (ii) to fill half the conduction band states. In each case state the position of the Fermi level and show the symmetry between vacant and filled states. In terms of symmetry show the qualitative dependence of each of these numbers and of the Fermi level positions on temperature. Show your work.

(b) At 0°K how many electrons are needed to fill 99.9% of the valence band levels? Determine $E_F - E_v$ at 0°K. What is the hole density p? The temperature is now raised to 292°K. Some electrons must be in the conduction band. Determine p and n, the pn product, and $E_F - E_v$ at 292°K. Note that $E_F - E_v$ is a function of temperature in this unsymmetric situation.

(c) How many kT wide is the energy gap? Express the number of electrons in the conduction band and the number of holes in the valence band each in terms of the *sums* of probabilities determined from Fermi statistics. In this case the sums can be computed as it is a simple geometric series. Determine the number of electrons in the conduction band as a function of the Fermi level. Put the summations in suitable integral form and show that the results are the same.

(d) The Fermi level is determined by the number of electrons present. Using *proper* graph paper plot the position of the Fermi level as a function of the number of electrons in the conduction band. (Should semilog paper be used?) Invert the plot showing the number of electrons versus Fermi level as the Fermi level varies continuously from $4\,kT$ above the valence band edge to $8\,kT$ above it. Plot the number of holes in the valence band on the *same* sheet as a function of the Fermi level. Plot the pn product for the same range of E_F. What is the value of $n_i{}^2$? Which statistics are adequate for making these calculations. Why?

V

THE STRUCTURE OF ATOMS

We begin the study of matter with the simplest forms and follow this with a qualitative approach to the more complicated situations. The qualitative studies are remarkably good over reasonable ranges.

THE SPHERICALLY SYMMETRICAL STATES OF THE HYDROGEN ATOM

With only a little mathematics or quantum mechanics we can solve some very simple cases of atomic structure. Such solutions clearly demonstrate certain quantum mechanical ideas and are, of course, also vital to the understanding of materials.

The hydrogen atom, made up of an electron and a proton, is thought of classically in terms of the electron going around the much heavier proton (or both going around their mutual center of mass). The electron and proton attract one another due to their opposite charge. If we neglect the very small proton motion, we can express the attraction of the electron to the proton as a simple potential energy well in which the electron is located. The potential energy V is given by

$$V = -\frac{q^2}{4\pi\epsilon_0 r} = -\frac{q^2}{4\pi\epsilon_0 \sqrt{x^2 + y^2 + z^2}} \qquad (5\text{-}1)$$

Here V is arbitrarily set at zero for r very large. The ϵ_0 is the permittivity of free space; no dielectric lies between the electron and proton.

77

Thus, for the electron of the hydrogen atom, we have

$$-\frac{\hbar^2}{2m}\left(\frac{\partial^2}{\partial x^2}+\frac{\partial^2}{\partial y^2}+\frac{\partial^2}{\partial z^2}\right)\psi - \frac{q^2\psi}{4\pi\epsilon_0\sqrt{x^2+y^2+z^2}} = E\psi \qquad (5\text{-}2)$$

This is clearly awkward and should be expressed in spherical coordinates. The equation, in vector notation, can then be written as

$$-\frac{\hbar^2}{2m}\nabla^2\psi - \frac{q^2}{4\pi\epsilon_0 r}\psi = E\psi \qquad (5\text{-}3)$$

For our present purposes we simplify the case even further by considering only solutions that are spherically symmetrical. The nonspherical character appears entirely in the vector operator ∇^2, the "Laplacian." Considering only the spherically symmetrical cases is a severe restriction, imposed only because of mathematical complications rather than because of physical limitations of our procedures. Nonspherical cases will be considered later. Since the sought for solutions are independent of the spherical coordinates θ and ϕ, the radially dependent equations are obtained by standard procedures found in various mathematics books. Then, by multiplying by $-2m/\hbar^2$ and transposing the E,

$$\frac{\partial^2\psi}{\partial r^2}+\frac{2}{r}\frac{\partial\psi}{\partial r}+\frac{2m}{\hbar^2}\left(E+\frac{q^2}{4\pi r\epsilon_0}\right)\psi = 0 \qquad (5\text{-}4)$$

The great importance of the Hamiltonian is now seen. A ψ function specifically for the hydrogen atom is determined by solution of equation (5-4). It is specific because of the limitations imposed by the potential energy function, which enters only through the Hamiltonian. It is necessary to find a solution for (5-4) bearing in mind that E is a constant.

Unquestionably the easiest way to solve differential equations is to know the form of the answer. In this case the simplest solution has the form

$$\psi = c\exp\left(\frac{-r}{a}\right) \qquad (5\text{-}5)$$

This can be checked and the constants a and c can be evaluated by substituting ψ from (5-5) in (5-4). It can be seen that c drops out:

$$0 = c(-a)^{-2}\exp\left(\frac{-r}{a}\right)+\frac{2}{r}\left(\frac{-1}{a}\right)c\exp\left(\frac{-r}{a}\right)$$

$$+\frac{2m}{\hbar^2}\left(E+\frac{q^2}{\epsilon_0 r4\pi}\right)c\exp\left(\frac{-r}{a}\right) \qquad (5\text{-}6)$$

Divide by $c \exp(-r/a)$:

$$a^{-2} - 2\frac{1}{ar} + \frac{2m}{\hbar^2}\left(E + \frac{q^2}{4\pi\epsilon_0 r}\right) = 0 \tag{5-7}$$

Now our ψ is *no solution* if E is dependent on r as it at first appears to be. However, we can find a value for a such that E is independent of r. This is done by setting the sum of those terms involving r equal to zero. We then have

$$\frac{2}{r}\left(-\frac{1}{a} + \frac{mq^2}{4\pi\epsilon_0 \hbar^2}\right) = 0 \tag{5-8}$$

which must be true for all values of r. We solve for a in (5-8), yielding

$$a = \frac{4\pi\hbar^2\epsilon_0}{mq^2} \tag{5-9}$$

The rest of equation (5-7) must then also be zero. Thus

$$a^{-2} + \frac{2mE}{\hbar^2} = 0$$

or

$$E = -\frac{\hbar^2}{2ma^2} \tag{5-10}$$

From our solution for a we then have

$$E = -\frac{mq^4}{32\pi^2\hbar^2\epsilon_0{}^2} \tag{5-11}$$

Our solution for the eigenfunction is

$$\psi_{1s} = c \exp\left(\frac{-rmq^2}{4\pi\hbar^2\epsilon_0}\right) \tag{5-12}$$

The subscript indicates the lowest energy in the "sharp" series (a spectrographic term).

Now this was a *real* physical problem and the results of quantum mechanics are capable of being measured. Remember that we chose V as zero for great separation of the electron and proton. Since the E value indicates that the electron is in a negative energy state, we must add this amount of energy to the atom to free the electron. This is therefore interpreted as the ionization energy of the atom. Putting in numbers (there are *no* arbitrary constants), we find that $E = 13.53$ eV $= (2.17 \times 10^{-18} J)$, a quantity known as the Rydberg (Ry). This is the measured value.

It is interesting that the preceding state function, designated above as ψ_{1s}, which is based on wave mechanics, is not wavelike. It *was* the atomic spectra that pointed out the need for a new mechanics with wavelike solutions.

Higher energy and less simple states can also be found in the spherically symmetric system. The equation to be solved is still (5-4) and we are looking for other solutions. A good trial function is

$$\psi_{2s} = ce^{-r/b}\left(1 - \frac{r}{b}\right) \tag{5-13}$$

Note that ψ_{2s} is zero at $r = b$. This zero value at the spherical surface constitutes what is known as a "nodal" surface. The term "node" usually refers to a point or small region of relatively little motion as is observed, for example, at points along a vibrating string. The simile is really seen to be excellent when one remembers that the ψ function also is "oscillating" with $\exp(-iEt/\hbar)$ and, further, the sign of the "displacement" changes as one goes through the nodal sphere. Other nodal surfaces are involved in nonspherical eigenfunctions.

By the same techniques of evaluation, it is found that $b = 2a$ and that $E_{2s} = E_{1s}/4$ where E_{1s} is the energy associated with ψ_{1s}. It is known as 1 Ry (one Rydberg). The energy E_{2s} is only one-fourth as negative as E_{1s} and therefore only one-fourth as much energy is needed to free an electron from this second state. It takes $\frac{3}{4}$ Ry (or 10.15 eV) to raise an electron from the lower 1s state to the higher 2s state. (This is not possible by light absorption in this case, however, because of certain other requirements of the process.)

It is highly instructive to plot ψ versus r (see Fig. 5-1). Note that ψ_{2s} has both a nodal surface and a maximum, whereas ψ_{1s} has neither. A study of how ψ oscillates around zero and how it ultimately goes asymptotically to zero leads us to conclude that for every maximum there is also a nodal surface.

Fig. 5-1 ψ is shown on this plot in a usual manner. The coordinates for each ψ plot is ψ itself versus r. It is plotted using its energy eigenvalue as a baseline. Note that ψ is finite in a region where the total energy is *less* than the potential energy. The potential energy is calculated as though the entire electronic charge were at a point. The apparent conflict is "settled" by realizing that, though this is the correct procedure for forming the Hamiltonian, the electron is not localized. The electron can only be "found" in such a region by experiments which add energy to it. Thus the electron is never "found" where its total energy is less than the potential energy. However, it has effective charge densities in these regions.

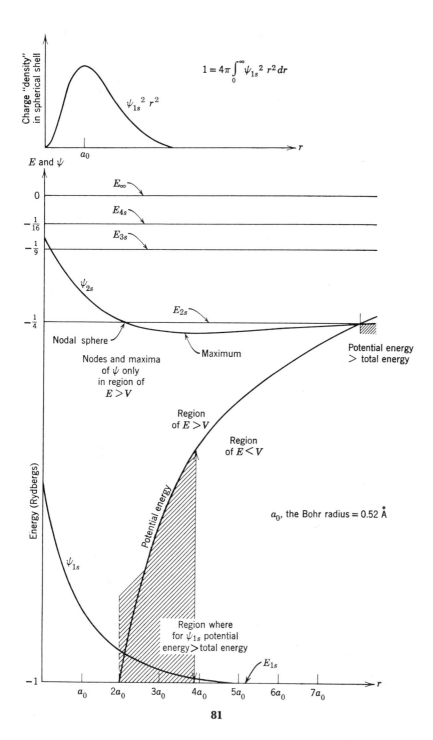

Charge "density" in spherical shell

$$1 = 4\pi \int_0^\infty \psi_{1s}^2\, r^2\, dr$$

$\psi_{1s}^2\, r^2$

a_0

r

E and ψ

0

E_∞

$-\frac{1}{16}$

E_{4s}

$-\frac{1}{9}$

E_{3s}

ψ_{2s}

E_{2s}

$-\frac{1}{4}$

Nodal sphere

Nodes and maxima of ψ only in region of $E > V$

Maximum

Potential energy $>$ total energy

Region of $E > V$

Region of $E < V$

a_0, the Bohr radius $= 0.52$ Å

Energy (Rydbergs)

Potential energy

ψ_{1s}

Region where for ψ_{1s} potential energy $>$ total energy

E_{1s}

-1

a_0 $2a_0$ $3a_0$ $4a_0$ $5a_0$ $6a_0$ $7a_0$

r

81

NONSPHERICAL HYDROGENIC STATES

The nonspherical states of hydrogen are, of course, more complicated and the mathematical methods are more involved. As will be seen, these states are not the lowest energy states and are therefore of interest in hydrogen in that they represent forms appropriate to *excited* electronic levels. "Excited" levels implies that these levels are reached by adding some energy to the lowest, or ground state, but not enough energy to ionize the system. If our atom system involved several electrons, then some electrons would have to occupy these higher energy states because of the Pauli exclusion principle. They would not be "excited" but would occupy states of about the same form as the excited states in hydrogen.

To go through the mathematical gymnastics involved in the solution of the excited hydrogen states serves two purposes. First, it is educational in itself in a mathematical sense, and, second, it gives a greater degree of familiarity of the subject to the student. It does have one major disadvantage, however: this is merely a side issue here and therefore distracts from our main path. We will therefore give the results only and point out that they can be checked easily and constants can be evaluated by putting them in the Schrödinger equation.*

The lowest energy nonspherical states are of the form

$$\psi_{2px} = c_{2p}\, xe^{-r/2a_0}, \qquad \psi_{2py} = c_{2p}\, ye^{-r/2a_0}, \qquad \psi_{2pz} = c_{2p}\, ze^{-r/2a_0} \qquad (5\text{-}14)$$

where c_{2p} is the normalizing constant. Note that ψ_{2px} is an odd function of x and has a nodal plane at $x = 0$. The 2_{py} and 2_{pz} functions have similar characteristics. These can be shown (see Problems 5, 6) to have identical energy to the $2s$ state represented by the stationary function

$$\psi_{2s} = c_{2s}\, e^{-r/2a_0}\!\left(\frac{r}{2a_0} - 1\right) \qquad (5\text{-}15)$$

Now ψ_{2s} has a zero or nodal surface at $r = 2a_0$. It is finite both inside and outside this spherical surface.

States of more complexity exist:

$$\psi_{3s} = c_{3s}\, e^{-r/3a_0}\!\left[2\!\left(\frac{r}{3a_0}\right)^{2} - 6\!\left(\frac{r}{3a_0}\right) + 3\right] \qquad (5\text{-}16)$$

and

$$\psi_{3px} = c_{3p}\, e^{-r/3a_0}\!\left(\frac{r}{3a_0} - 2\right)x \qquad (5\text{-}17)$$

---

* The Schrödinger equation in spherical coordinates for stationary states, where $x = r \sin\theta \cos\phi,\, y = r\sin\theta\sin\phi,\, z = r\cos\theta$:

$$-\frac{\hbar^2}{2m}\!\left[\frac{1}{r^2}\frac{\partial}{\partial r}\!\left(r^2\frac{\partial}{\partial r}\right) + \frac{1}{r^2\sin\theta}\frac{\partial}{\partial\theta}\!\left(\sin\theta\frac{\partial}{\partial\theta}\right) + \frac{1}{r^2\sin^2\theta}\frac{\partial^2}{\partial\phi^2}\right]\psi - \left(\frac{q^2}{4\pi\epsilon_0 r} + E\right)\psi = 0$$

where again y or z may be substituted for x. Note that ψ_{3px} has a nodal plane at $x = 0$, is an odd function of x, and has a nodal sphere at $r = 6a_0$. The subscripts 1, 2, and 3 on the state functions are known as the *principal quantum numbers*.

Two general comments are in order. First, the energy goes up with the complexity of the wave function ψ. It will be noted that the p functions have almost the identical *spherical* complexity that the s function of one lower principal quantum number have. The p functions have *directional* complexity, however, which makes up for their spherical simplicity. The number of nodal surfaces of a ψ function is, in every case, one less than the principal quantum number. The s functions, being spherically symmetric, have spherical nodal surfaces. The p functions have one nodal plane and any additional nodal surfaces are spherical. The second general comment has to do with the exponent of the exponential in the wave functions. The *radius* of the ψ function increases directly with the principal quantum number. (That is, the larger the principal quantum numbers, the larger the radii.)

Even more complicated functions exist for higher quantum states. The next of interest is the d state. For each quantum number n there are two s states (which differ only in spin), for $n > 1$ there are three pairs of p states, for $n > 2$ there are five pairs of d states, and so forth. The d states are seen to start with the principal quantum number 3, and, because they are even more complicated angularly than are the p states, they have greater spherical simplicity:

$$\psi_{3d} = c_{3d} e^{-r/3a_0} \Lambda \tag{5-18}$$

where Λ takes on any of the five quadratic forms

$$2xy, \quad 2yz, \quad 2zx, \quad x^2 - y^2, \quad \text{or} \quad \frac{3z^2 - r^2}{\sqrt{3}} \tag{5-19}$$

where $r^2 = x^2 + y^2 + z^2$.

These obviously are not symmetrical in $x, y,$ and z. The first four coefficients are hyperbolic cylinders and the fifth is a hyperboloid of revolution of two sheets. Each of the ψs has nodal surfaces, the first four have two intersecting planes, and the fifth has a cone.

STRUCTURE OF LARGER ATOMS

Consider an atom having several protons. In the neutral state the atom will have electrons around it equal in number to the protons in the nucleus. It will also have neutrons with no coulombic influence on the potential energy term in the Hamiltonian. When only one electron is involved, that is, all others are stripped off by ionization processes, the entire treatment of the hydrogen atom is applicable by simply considering the Z proton positive charge in the nucleus. The Schrödinger equation for the nearly stripped large atom then becomes

$$-\frac{\hbar^2}{2m}\nabla^2\psi - \left(\frac{Zq^2}{4\pi\epsilon_0 r} + E\right)\psi = 0 \qquad (5\text{-}20)$$

It then can be verified that, for the one-electron situation, all radii are then divided by Z and all energy magnitudes become Z^2 times as large.

When we consider more than one electron in these larger atoms, we must take into account Postulates VII and VIII (Spin and Exclusion Principle). Two electrons cannot be in the same state—but two states may differ only in the parameter referred to as "spin." Only two values of spin are possible. Helium's two electrons can fit into the lowest states, but, in larger atoms (or ions), when two electrons have filled the two spatially identical states having the lowest energy, further electrons must go into states of higher energy. Actually things are not this simple as we have neglected the interaction between the electrons.

THE ELECTRON SHIELDING APPROXIMATION

As in ordinary mechanics, problems of many bodies also become complicated in quantum mechanics. And, as in many-bodied classical problems, the multielectron atom is "solved" by approximational methods. We note that one electron (of negative charge) "shields" a second electron from the full strength of the positively charged nucleus. Careful treatment will yield a fair idea of the extent of this effect. An atom with 15 protons (phosphorus) has two electrons very close to the core. The two electrons in the next quantum energy level, a $2s$ shell, "see" a net charge of only about 13 protons as the lower energy electrons are very close to the nucleus and, to the extent of their charge, they balance its effects. Similarly, electrons further out feel the effect of an even smaller nuclear charge. The fact is, however, that $2s$ electrons have some charge close to the core and this charge is not effectively shielded from the proton core by the $1s$ electrons. The degree of this "penetration" varies with the class of the outer electrons (see Fig. 5.2 and Problem 5-9).

We can tabulate the electrons and their approximate shielding properties (Table 5-1). These produce fair results for atoms having small numbers of electrons but get progressively worse for larger atoms. Nevertheless, we get a better picture of the whole system by this technique of shielding cal-

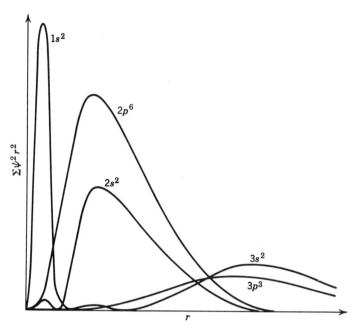

Fig. 5-2   Radial distribution of charge for various electron types in phosphorus. Note that no shell *completely* shields outer shells from the nucleus and that there exists some "reverse" shielding.

TABLE 5-1   SHIELDING COEFFICIENTS

Shielded Electron	Shielding Electron		
	$1s$	$2s$ or $2p$ [a]	$3s$ or $3p$ [a]
$1s$	0.29	0	0
$2s$ or $2p$ [a]	0.87	0.29	0
$3s$ or $3p$ [a]	1.00	0.87	0.29

[a] It should be noted that s and p states are lumped together, whereas it is clear from equations (5-14) to (5-17) that s states have a charge density at the origin, whereas $\psi\psi^*$ for the p states shows zero charge density at the origin and a quadratic increase away from it. Thus penetration and shielding should clearly be different.

culations. According to the scheme of Table 5-1 the energy is readily calculated. We have, in Rydberg units (1 Ry = 13.53 eV),

$$U = -\frac{(Z - Z_0)^2}{n^2} \text{ Ry} \tag{5-21}$$

The denominator n is the principal quantum number of the electron whose energy is to be computed. The shielding factors of all the electrons other than the one being shielded are added to calculate Z_0. The atomic number Z (e.g., 15 for phosphorus) is known. The energy U is that of an electron (or average electron in a shell) relative to the free electron level. For example, if there are five electrons in the same shell, the energy of the shell is $5U$, a negative number, indicating binding.

If an electron is removed from the shell, each of the remaining four electrons will have somewhat less shielding and therefore will be bound

TABLE 5-2   ELECTRON CONFIGURATION OF LIGHT ELEMENTS

Atomic Number Z	Name and Symbol		$1s$	$2s$	$2p$	$3s$	$3p$	$4s$		Ionization Energy (eV)
1	Hydrogen	H	1							13.53
2	Helium	He	2							24.46
3	Lithium	Li	2	1						5.36
4	Beryllium	Be	2	2						9.28
5	Boron	B	2	2	1					8.26
6	Carbon	C	2	2	2					11.22
7	Nitrogen	N	2	2	3				Half-filled p shell	14.48
8	Oxygen	O	2	2	4					13.55
9	Fluorine	F	2	2	5					17.34
10	Neon	Ne	2	2	6					21.47
11	Sodium	Na	2	2	6	1				5.12
12	Magnesium	Mg	2	2	6	2				7.61
13	Aluminum	Al	2	2	6	2	1			5.96
14	Silicon	Si	2	2	6	2	2			8.12
15	Phosphorus	P	2	2	6	2	3		Half-filled p shell	10.9
16	Sulphur	S	2	2	6	2	4			10.30
17	Chlorine	Cl	2	2	6	2	5			12.95
18	Argon	Ar (or A)	2	2	6	2	6			15.68
19	Potassium	K	2	2	6	2	6	1		4.32
20	Calcium	Ca	2	2	6	2	6	2		6.09

Note: 3d shell starts filling with $Z = 21$.

more strongly. After a single ionization the shell energy would be $4U_1$. The free electron will have zero energy. (No kinetic energy, as just enough energy to free it was added, and no potential by the definition of the zero of potential energy).

This change of total energy is the energy for ionization. It can be expressed as

$$\text{ionization energy} = 4U_1 - 5U \qquad (5\text{-}22)$$

where both U_1 and U are negative numbers. Clearly, the energy after, minus the energy before, is the energy that must be added.

Consider Be (beryllium), $Z = 4$. The $2s$ shell has two electrons which are shielded from the 4 proton nucleus by the $1s$ shell at the rate of 0.87 reduction in effective nuclear charge per $1s$ electron. Each of the $2s$ electrons is shielded by the other to the extent of 0.29 charges. Thus

$$Z_0 = 2 \times (0.87) + 0.29 = 2.03$$

The principal quantum number, n, is 2. Thus each electron is below the zero energy level and

$$U = -\frac{(4 - 2.03)^2}{2^2} = -\frac{1.97^2}{4} = -0.97 \text{ Ry}$$

Since there are two electrons, the shell energy is

$$-1.94 \text{ Ry}$$

After one electron is removed by ionization, the second electron is shielded only by the remaining $1s$ electrons, thus Z_0 is 1.74 electronic charges. Then

$$U_1 = -\frac{(4 - 1.74)^2}{4} = -1.28 \text{ Ry}$$

This is the total shell energy since there is only one electron involved.

The total energy required for the removal of the $2s$ electron is then the energy after removal minus that before removal. The computed ionization energy is then

$$-1.28 \text{ Ry} - (-1.94 \text{ Ry}) = 0.66 \text{ Ry}$$

The observed ionization energy is 0.68 Ry. This should not be construed to " prove " the method as the shielding was chosen to fit this type of case.

Sometimes more than one shell is involved in the process; in this case all shells must be considered. It is the entire system that is involved. As an example consider the ionization of a nitrogen atom.

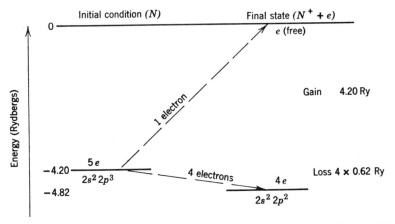

Fig. 5-3 Not shown: $1s^2$ level (45 Ry down) (unchanged by ionization). Computed ionization value. The superscripts indicate the number of electrons in each spatial state type.

$$4(-4.82)_{(final)} - 5(-4.20)_{(initial)} = 1.72 \text{ Ry}$$

The energy diagram of Fig. 5-3 shows one way of keeping tab of the energy. Actually $2p$ and $2s$ states do not have the same ionization energy. Experiment yields values of 1.90 Ry for $2s$ and 1.07 Ry for $2p$ electrons. (Note that the $2s$ is more strongly bound because of its greater penetration, as discussed above.) It is clear these computations give results that are too naive.

IONIC BINDING

A simple approach to the chemical interaction of two atoms by the formation of ions can be made. How much lower will the total energy be if two atoms act together to form ions? No attraction as such is to be considered here, so this is not really a binding problem. Only the energy reduction resulting from the formation of ions will be calculated. However, the ions thus formed cannot be separated en masse since large static forces would be involved. Thus the energy freed by the production of ions must be restored to the system before the atoms can be pulled apart. This ion formation process is closely related to a binding energy. We will be using lithium and fluorine in our example.

Consider atoms of Li and F reacting to give Li^+F^- (see Fig. 5-4). The reaction product equation indicates that one lithium atom plus one fluorine atom will produce the lithium fluoride. It should not be assumed, however, that the atoms are paired in the resulting structure.

Crystals of LiF are of the so-called face-centered cube structure. The Li

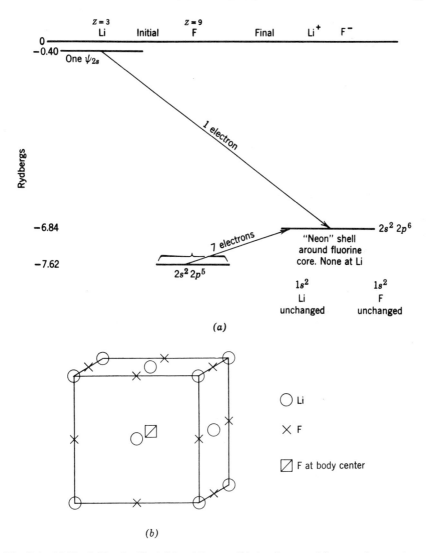

Fig. 5-4 (a) The $1s^2$ levels of both Li and F are well below bottom of figure and are unchanged. (b) A unit cube of LiF salt.

ions are at the cube corners and face-centers and the F ions are at the edge centers and body centers (centers of cubes). A study of stacked cubes will show that the F ions are arranged just as the Li ions, but displaced by one-half of a cube edge length from them in the x direction (for example). Lithium ions have six nearest neighbor F ions and vice versa. The crystal cannot be construed to be built up of LiF molecules since no preferred pairing exists in the crystal.

The inner electrons are not shown in the figure. The initial condition is calculated on the basis of the isolated neutral atoms; the final condition on the isolated charged atoms:

$$7 \text{ electrons are raised } 0.78 \text{ Ry each} \qquad (5.46 \text{ Ry})$$
$$1 \text{ electron is lowered } 6.44 \text{ Ry} \qquad (-6.44 \text{ Ry})$$

computed energy of reaction = computed net *decrease* in energy = +.98 Ry
actual measured reaction energy = 0.43 Ry
(using thermochemical means.)

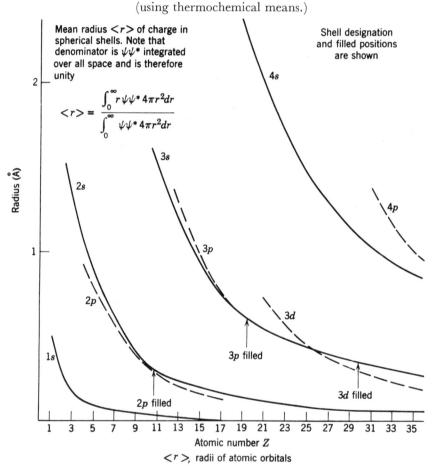

Fig. 5-5 Radii of Atomic Orbitals (in Ångstroms). In forming filled shells the electrons do not repel each other as much as the added proton attracts them. As a result, the shells shrink. The shell radius, in units of .52 Å—the Bohr radius for hydrogen—is given approximately by $r = nU^{-1/2}$.

The shielding constants are neither good enough nor of the best form to show the correct net energy lowering where so many electrons are involved. Furthermore, in the dense state found among interacting atoms, the isolated atom is not the appropriate structure for either the initial or final computation.

Other factors are also involved in the chemical binding of ionic crystals. In forming bonds between ions, the ions attract opposites and repel their own kind because of their charges. This further modifies the energy of the system.

The ideas of shielding were initially developed to understand atoms larger and more complex than hydrogen. It is clear from the discussion thus far that the nuclear charge is only partially shielded from the electrons by other outer electrons. Thus to all electrons the attraction is very large; in fact, the larger the number of electrons in a shell, the larger the effective nuclear charge. Since d shells have ten electrons each (as compared to six electrons in a p shell) the d shell in particular will shrink as more electrons are added. Figure 5-5 shows this effect.

PROBLEMS

1. Show that $b = 2a_0$ and $E_{2s} = \frac{1}{4}$ Ry for ψ_{2s}.
2. For what value or values of r do $\psi_{1s}^2 r^2$ and $\psi_{2s}^2 r^2$ have maximum values?
3. Evaluate c in equation (5-12).
4. Show that $\psi_{2pz} = c_{2p} z e^{-r/2a_0}$ is a solution to the Schrödinger equation for hydrogen. (Hint: Put z in spherical coordinates.)
5. Find E_{2px} from equations (5-14).
6. Find E_{3px} and E_{3s}.
7. Find the nodal (zero) surfaces for the s, p, and d states for principal quantum numbers 1, 2, and 3.
8. What fraction of an electronic charge is inside the first nodal surface for a ψ_{2s} state? This charge will influence $1s$ states somewhat and will not be shielded appreciably by $2p$, as seen below. What fraction of an electronic charge is inside this same surface for a ψ_{2p} state?
9. Show that the two conclusions following equation (5-20) are valid.
10. Compute the energy for ionizing one electron from boron ($Z = 5$).
11. Find the *binding* energy of a sixth electron to boron. Can it be assumed that the sixth electron would be in an $n = 2$ state?
12. In the compound LiF, the interatomic distance is about 2.0 Å.
    (a) If it is assumed that a Li^{+1} ion and a F^{-1} ion are brought this close

together, what binding energy do these have? (This is in addition
to energy needed to produce ions.)

(b) Using appropriate shielding values, plot the ψ functions for the
$F^{-1} 2px$ state, assuming that the Li^{+1} ion is at $x = 2$ Å from an
origin of the fluorine atom.

(c) Plot, on the same figure, the $2s$ function for neutral Li. Is the shift
of the electron from Li^0 to F^{-1} as great as might be implied by
simple ideas?

13. Plot the effective nuclear charge for the $2s$ and $2p$ electrons as a function
of Z (in the ranges $Z = 3$ to $Z = 10$). Assume that the atoms are
neutral.

VI

THE COVALENT BOND

BINDING OF CLOSELY SPACED ATOMS WITHOUT CHARGE TRANSFER

In this chapter we first show how the state functions account for the directional bonding found in "dense" materials. The means of determining the correct functions, however, is only touched upon. The variational method and many dimensional spaces are introduced. Though here covalent bonds and ionic bonds are treated separately, actually there are very few natural examples of completely covalent or purely ionic bonding.

DIRECTIONAL CHARACTER OF BONDS AND NONADDITIVITY OF CHARGE

We have noted previously that the effect of several possible states is determined by adding their state functions. In the same way, the "character" of an electron in an atom can be found by adding the various possible p states and s states, with suitable coefficients. Let us assume that the three p states are equally likely to be occupied by our electron. A suitable state function, then, is a sum of the individual eigenfunctions.

For example, carbon* has two electrons in the $1s$ state, designated $1s^2$, and four other electrons. The usual state of the carbon atom *in a molecule*

---

* Note that carbon, silicon, and germanium are all in group IV of the periodic chart.

involves one $2s$ state and three $2p$ states sometimes called the sp^3 state of the atom. Now the p wave functions had the *form*

$$\psi_x = c_{px}\, xe^{-r/r_0}$$
$$\psi_y = c_{py}\, ye^{-r/r_0}$$
$$\psi_z = c_{pz}\, ze^{-r/r_0}$$

and the s wave function has the form

$$\psi_s = c_s e^{-r/r_0}\left(\frac{r}{r_0} - 1\right) = \frac{c_s}{r_0}(r - r_0)e^{-r/r_0}$$

(6-1)

In its rewritten form the quantity c_s/r_0 is dimensionally, and otherwise on a par with c_{px}, and so on.

Because of symmetry the coefficients c_{px}, c_{py}, and c_{pz} must be equal in magnitude $(=c_p)$. In equation (6-1), r_0 has been used in place of $2a_0$ for the hydrogenic p states, allowing for the extra nuclear charge, for the shielding by the inner core electrons (the $1s$ electrons), and for the intrashell shielding. We have used the same r_0 for the $2s$ state as for the $2p$ states. (This is undoubtedly not precise because the shielding is not identical for these two situations. It is seen in the footnote of Table 5-1 that the s states involve more charge toward the center than do p states.) Suitable state functions can be formed by linear combinations of the s and p functions. Then

$$\psi = c_x\psi_x + c_y\psi_y + c_z\psi_z + c_s\psi_s \tag{6-2}$$

The particular symmetric combinations known as the sp^3 states are:

$$\psi_{111} = c_{111}[\psi_x + \psi_y + \psi_z + \psi_s] = c_{111}\, e^{-r/r_0}[+x + y + z + \alpha(r - r_0)]$$
$$\psi_{1\bar{1}\bar{1}} = c_{111}\, e^{-r/r_0}[+x - y - z + \alpha(r - r_0)]$$
$$\psi_{\bar{1}1\bar{1}} = c_{111}\, e^{-r/r_0}[-x + y - z + \alpha(r - r_0)]$$
$$\psi_{\bar{1}\bar{1}1} = c_{111}\, e^{-r/r_0}[-x - y + z + \alpha(r - r_0)]$$

(6-3)

The subscripts on the ψs denote the signs of the component px, py, and pz functions.

From chemical considerations we know that their valence properties are therefore somewhat alike. Where carbon has an "outer shell" of $2s$ and $2p$ states, silicon has $3s$ and $3p$ and germanium $4s$ and $4p$ states. The $2s^12p^3$, $3s^13p^3$, and $4s^14p^3$ are then the sp^3 states involved in covalent bonding in carbon, silicon, and germanium, respectively. "Inner core" electrons are: $1s^2$ for carbon; $1s^2$, $2s^22p^6$ for silicon; $1s^2$, $2s^2$, $2p^6$, $3s^2$, $3p^6$, $3d^{10}$ for germanium.

Note that we can solve for the s and p states in terms of the sp^3 states. Thus

$$\psi_s = \frac{1}{4c_{111}} (\psi_{111} + \psi_{1\bar{1}\bar{1}} + \psi_{\bar{1}1\bar{1}} + \psi_{\bar{1}\bar{1}1})$$

$$\psi_x = \frac{1}{4c_{111}} (\psi_{111} + \psi_{1\bar{1}\bar{1}} - \psi_{\bar{1}1\bar{1}} - \psi_{\bar{1}\bar{1}1})$$

$$\psi_y = \frac{1}{4c_{111}} (\psi_{111} - \psi_{1\bar{1}\bar{1}} + \psi_{\bar{1}1\bar{1}} - \psi_{\bar{1}\bar{1}1})$$

$$\psi_z = \frac{1}{4c_{111}} (\psi_{111} - \psi_{1\bar{1}\bar{1}} - \psi_{\bar{1}1\bar{1}} + \psi_{\bar{1}\bar{1}1})$$

Since all these systems can be expanded in terms of the s and p functions, it must also be possible to expand all s and p state functions in terms of the sp^3 type state functions. Nowhere in quantum mechanics is there any criterion for deciding that one solution is more fundamental than another. Therefore it should be understood that only because of convenience or simplicity is one set of orthogonal solutions preferred to another. Pauling has stated that, if quantum mechanics had been developed by chemists instead of spectroscopists, the sp^3 states might have been the "standard" forms.

For the sp^3 states to be useful in expansions they must be energy eigenfunctions. This requires that there be a unique energy for each eigenfunction, but we have already seen that the p and s functions have only approximately the same energy. The energy of the s function is somewhat lower in its ground state. The sp^3 eigenfunctions, then, must be excited states of the free atom rather than the lowest energy states.

The eigenvalue property of sp^3 states is clearly needed for their directional nature to be of value. It is because the s and p states have the identically same energy that they stay in phase. If the frequencies were different the directions would not be constant.

The perturbation of one atom by another causes a substantial reduction in total energy for the sp^3 states. Their directional characteristic, which is discussed below, permits them to have the lowest energy for the interaction of certain atoms, even though it is above the lowest energy for the isolated atom. In those situations where the sp^3 states are the lowest in energy, they will dominate and their directional properties will control the structure involved.

One of the very important results of addition of states becomes apparent. Let us consider the ψ_{111} state function. The three p states add in such a way

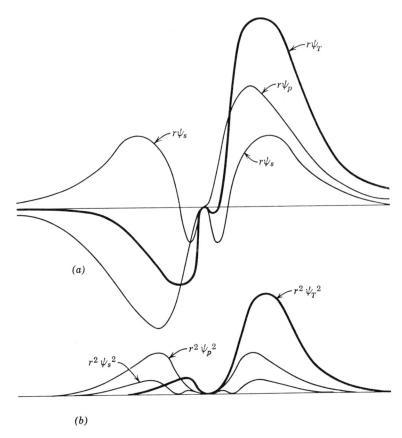

Fig. 6-1 Outside the first nodal sphere the positive s state has a cancellation effect on the negative lobe of the p state while at the same time it enhances the positive p lobe. The enhancement is reversed inside this nodal sphere. The "charge" is thus unsymmetrical in the summed situation, whereas each "component" represents a symmetrical charge. (The ψ functions as shown are multiplied by the radius to "correct" for the larger volume at greater radius.)

that they are all positive in the $+x$, $+y$, $+z$ octant and all negative in the $-x$, $-y$, $-z$ octant. Beyond the nodal sphere the s state, however, is positive in all octants. Thus it adds to the p states, enhancing the overall magnitude in the $(+ + +)$ octant, and has the opposite effect in the $(- - -)$ octant, diminishing the magnitude there.* The electronic charge density, being proportional to the square of the magnitude of ψ, is therefore substantially

* See Fig. 6-1 for reversal of this inside the radial nodal sphere. Only 5% of the "charge" of the $2s$ state is inside, and even less of the p state is.

larger in the positive than in the negative octant. This can perhaps be visualized better by considering a single p and s state. Figure 6-1a shows the value of ψ along the axis of the p state. The s state is symmetrical, having no angular dependence, whereas the p state is antisymmetrical. Thus they "add" on one side and "subtract" on the other. This makes the lobes very one sided. In the sp^3 system, where the p lobes sum to give a cube diagonal directionality, the added s state greatly reduces the value in one octant while increasing it in the other. As a result the total atomic sp^3 state has four intense lobes with considerable directionality.

The significance of this additive character of ψs as compared to adding the "charge densities," $\psi\psi^*$s, is very clear in this case. If the independent $\psi\psi^*$s were additive we would have

$$\psi_s\psi_s^* + \psi_x\psi_x^* + \psi_y\psi_y^* + \psi_z\psi_z^* = \left[c_s c_s^* \left(1 - \frac{r}{r_0} \right)^2 + c_p c_p^* (x^2 + y^2 + z^2) \right] e^{-r/r_0}$$

Since $x^2 + y^2 + z^2 = r^2$, this sum is completely symmetric spherically instead of having any directional characteristic. Thus in the additive nature of the eigenfunctions of quantum mechanics lies the secret of the nonspherical character since, if "charges" were additive, the atoms would demonstrate a spherical characteristic.

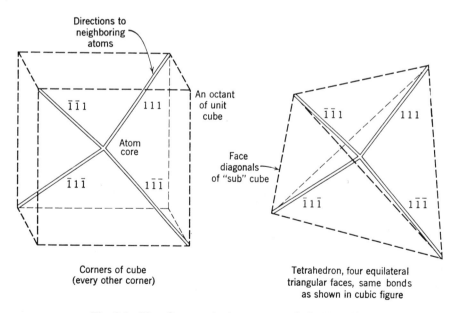

Fig. 6-2 The sp^3 states, also known as tetrahedral hybrids.

We then see that the linear nature of the system, which permits simple addition of solutions, *precludes* the simple adding of charges. Thus, we cannot think in terms of the effect of electrons acting on one another as though each had its own charge distribution. The system *does not* conserve the particle concept of charge distribution.

Notice the relative *directions* of these ψ_{111} type functions. Note that the system involving sp^3 states, shown in Fig. 6-2, has tetrahedral symmetry. And of course carbon has this symmetry in most compounds. Silicon and germanium have this symmetry with even fewer exceptions than does carbon. Though elemental carbon has the diamond form, which is tetrahedral, it also has a graphite form. Germanium and silicon crystals have only the diamond form when elemental.

The simple p functions of Fig. 6-2 are individually at right angles to one another so that one might expect 90° bonds in some structures. Many simple cubic compounds do have this structure. A special case is the molecule of H_2O (which is not cubic). The bonds between the two hydrogen atoms are actually 105° apart instead of 90°. This can be thought of as an "attempt" to have two p type bonds but the attempt is thwarted to a certain extent because of the Coulombic repulsion of the two positively charged hydrogen nuclei (simple protons in the case of hydrogen). The electrons do not shield the protons from one another well, being located, as they are, largely between the protons and the oxygen atom. This is shown in Fig. 6-3.

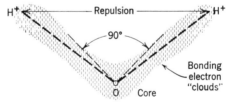

Fig. 6-3 The water molecule. The hydrogen bonds are 105° apart due to unshielded repulsion.

SATURATION OF BONDS

Figures 6-2 and 6-3 have not been explained in detail in the foregoing remarks. The p states can be drawn as in Fig. 6-4. The positive and negative directions of the charge lobes are identical except for the state function sign. Some s state addition can make the two lobes unsymmetrical but, when they are symmetrical, we would expect equally good bonding in the opposite direction from each one shown (Fig. 6-3). This does *not* happen. The bonds

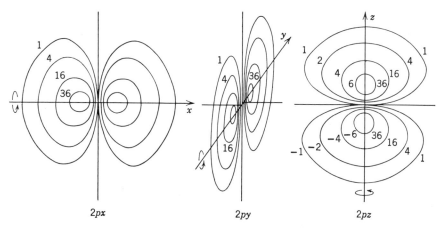

Fig. 6-4 Cross sections of three-dimensional figures of $2p$ states. Contours of $|\psi|$ and of constant charge density $|\psi|^2$ are shown. The complete set of contour is obtained by rotations around the $x, y,$ and z axes, respectively. Relative $|\psi|$ and $|\psi|^2$ are indicated.

are said to saturate. The *total* story of saturation, bonding energies, and so forth, is subtle, but a crude idea of the nature of saturation and bonding energies can be obtained from a simple picture. In order to see this more clearly let us examine a situation involving only s states (which are symmetrical).

Consider the case where two atoms approach one another. The electronic interaction between the two atoms can be studied, first, by finding the most suitable low-energy state function for the electrons. As a crude approximation, we consider the state of a *single* electron as an appropriate sum of the original s state functions, one from each atom. The single electron has a spin. Thus a single experiment must find this spin independent of the component state the electron is found in. The spin expectation value is this single value of spin and this can be achieved only if each of the component states has this same single spin. Then a part of being "appropriate" involves the spin corresponding to the states, both states must have the same spin. Subscripts designate the atom for which the particular s state function is appropriate, that is, ψ_a is centered on atom a:

$$\psi = c_1(\psi_a + \psi_b) \tag{6-4}$$

Both ψ_a and ψ_b are functions of position, of course, so the density of charge at any point will be

$$\psi\psi^* = c_1 c_1^*(\psi_a \psi_a^* + \psi_a \psi_b^* + \psi_b \psi_a^* + \psi_b \psi_b^*) \tag{6-5}$$

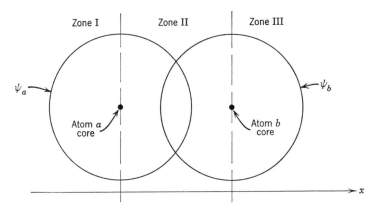

Fig. 6-5   Isomagnitude contours of ψ_a and ψ_b.

In order to evaluate c_1 of equation (6-5) it is necessary to normalize the state function. Integrating equation (6-5) over all space we obtain, for the left side,

$$\int \psi\psi^* \, d\tau = 1 \tag{6-6}$$

The right side is more complicated. We use the ideas of Fig. 6-5 and integrate over one zone at a time. In zone I we have assumed that $\psi = \psi_a$ and, in zone II, that $\psi = \psi_b$. Thus in zone I, for example, we have

$$\int \psi\psi^* \, d\tau = \int \psi_a\psi_a^* \, d\tau = \tfrac{1}{2} \tag{6-7}$$

The function $\psi_a\psi_a^*$ is symmetrical about the zone boundary and its total integral over all space is *one*, so the integration must yield $\tfrac{1}{2}$ in zone I alone, and, of course it must also integrate to $\tfrac{1}{2}$ in the rest of space. Thus the integration of (6-5) yields

$$1 = c_1 c_1^* \left[\tfrac{1}{2} + \int_{\text{II}} \psi_a\psi_a^* \, d\tau + \int_{\text{II}} \psi_b\psi_b^* \, d\tau + \int_{\text{II}} (\psi_a\psi_b^* + \psi_b\psi_a^*) d\tau + \tfrac{1}{2} \right]$$

as the statements relative to ψ_a in zone I hold equally well for ψ_b in zone III. Then

$$1 = c_1 c_1^* \left(1 + 2 \int_{\text{II}} \psi_a\psi_b^* \, d\tau + 2 \int_{\text{II}} \psi_a\psi_a^* \, d\tau \right) \tag{6-8}$$

Here, due to our assumed symmetry, we have equated the integrals

$$\int_{\text{II}} \psi_a\psi_b^* \, d\tau = \int_{\text{II}} \psi_b\psi_a^* \, d\tau \qquad \text{and} \qquad \int_{\text{II}} \psi_b\psi_b^* \, d\tau = \int_{\text{II}} \psi_a\psi_a^* \, d\tau$$

Although ψ_a and ψ_b will be either symmetric or antisymmetric (sign reversal) with each other, we make the added assumption that they are, everywhere in zone II, equal in magnitude. This assumption, that $\psi_a = \pm\psi_b$ at all points in zone II, is in substantial error and will cause the computed value of the integral to be considerably too large in magnitude. The conclusions we draw will, as a result, be somewhat exaggerated. The character of the system will be correct, however. In making this approximation we conclude that

$$\int_{\text{II}} \psi_a \psi_b^* \, d\tau = \pm \int_{\text{II}} \psi_a \psi_a^* \, d\tau = \pm\tfrac{1}{2} \tag{6-9}$$

The value of $\tfrac{1}{2}$ again is just the balance of the total space integral, remembering that ψ_a is zero in zone III.

We have thus evaluated all terms in equation (6-8):

$$1 = c_1 c_1^* [1 \pm 2(\tfrac{1}{2}) + 2(\tfrac{1}{2})] = 3c_1 c_1^* \quad \text{(symmetric)}$$
$$= c_1 c_1^* \quad \text{(antisymmetric)} \tag{6-10}$$

From this we find $c_1 c_1^*$ equals *one* in the antisymmetric case and *one-third* in the symmetric case. Thus we find the situation shown in Table 6-1.

TABLE 6-1

	Zone I	Zone II	Zone III
ψ symmetric	$\dfrac{1}{\sqrt{3}}\psi(x)$	$\dfrac{2}{\sqrt{3}}\psi(x)$	$\dfrac{1}{\sqrt{3}}\psi(-x)$
$\int \psi_s \psi_s^* \, d\tau$	$\tfrac{1}{6}$	$\tfrac{2}{3}$	$\tfrac{1}{6}$
ψ antisymmetric	$\psi(x)$	0	$-\psi(-x)$
$\int \psi_{as} \psi_{as}^* \, d\tau$	$\tfrac{1}{2}$	0	$\tfrac{1}{2}$

The symmetric case has $\tfrac{2}{3}$ of an electronic charge between the two protons thus effectively shielding them from each other's Coulombic forces. The net result will be an attraction. In the antisymmetric case the protonic charges are directly exposed to one another as there is no shielding negative charge between them.

In the antisymmetric case, where the electronic charge is depleted from between them and the nuclei are directly exposed to one another, the protons repel one another violently. This is clearly unstable. The antisymmetric situation can arise only during a collision. The two atoms involved would,

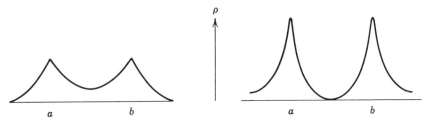

Fig. 6-6   Distribution of charge along interatomic axis. The curves are for H_2^+ ion, involving only one electron. Case (1): binding. Case (2): repulsion in collision.

of course, bounce off one another elastically. The two cases of charge distribution are shown schematically in Fig. 6-6 with a somewhat more precise distribution.

As discussed earlier, an electron has only one spin so it is clear that the atomic states which "contribute" to the molecular state must have the same spin. Thus when two hydrogen atoms, each with its electron, approach one another the occupied levels in the two atoms must have opposite spin if binding is to take place. Only under this condition will the unoccupied state of an atom be able to accommodate the electron from the other atom.

The bonds are strongest (i.e., the resultant energies of the electrons are lowest) when the bonds are most directional. As a result atoms prefer to form certain directional bonds. Atoms of large atomic number have greater difficulty forming directional bonds. When the potential energy in some region of space is low, the electrons crowd into that region and the occupied states have low energy. This is seen particularly near the core of large atoms. The large Z value reduces the orbital radii of inner state electrons and their binding energy gets to be very high. The converse is also true: when the electronic charge is highly concentrated it must be because the occupied states corresponding to this high concentration have low energy. As a result it is sufficient to look for combinations of states between atoms which will produce high charge density in order to find low energy states. And these low energy states result in interatomic binding as, to separate the atoms, large amounts of energy must be added to the electronic system to put the electrons in the higher energy ground states of the free atoms. The directional states have higher density of charge than the spherically symmetrical states. As a result, "spherical" atoms are more "metallic." That is, the electrons act more as distributed than as localized particles.

Thus we find, due to the additive nature of the state functions, that the electron is, to a disproportionate extent, *between* the two H atoms. Very little is left over for bonding to other atoms. As a result the bond is *saturated*.

Only one electron was involved in these calculations. The spin of state functions ψ_a and ψ_b were the same, clearly leaving room for a second electron having ψ_a and ψ_b of the opposite spin, where *both* electrons will go between the atoms. The principal effect of the second electron involves a Coulombic repulsion between the two electrons, and this must be taken into account. The calculation involving two electrons is too complicated for this book. It is through consideration of this case, however, that the simplicity of the Pauli exclusion principle becomes apparent.

MINIMUM ENERGY EIGENFUNCTIONS

We have thus far discussed the effects of the superposition of the linear state functions without any questions as to how the combinations are selected. We have implied that the strongest bonds are formed when the electronic energies are lowest and we have stated, more or less categorically, that bond strength and directional properties are closely related.

For approximation purposes we select that linear combination of state functions which yields the minimum energy (pragmatically this produces good results and therefore is probably essentially correct). This is not hard to accept due to its close tie with classical ideas. In quantum mechanics this is done by use of the mean value theorem (see Chapter II).

If a state ψ is expressed as the linear combination of two other functions ψ_a and ψ_b such that

$$\psi = c_a \psi_a + c_b \psi_b \tag{6-11}$$

we select c_a and c_b to minimize the energy of the state defined by ψ. This is done by

$$\frac{d\langle E \rangle}{dc_a} = 0 = \frac{d}{dc_a} \int (c_a \psi_a + c_b \psi_b) \hat{H}(c_a^* \psi_a^* + c_b^* \psi_b^*) \, d\tau \tag{6-12}$$

Equation (6-12) can be seen to be satisfied by the minimum average energy, that is, the minimum expectation value of the energy. Of course ψ must be normalized, and this requirement, along with equation (6-11), is used to define dc_b/dc_a that appears in the differentiation of the mean value integral of equation (6-12). It is found that the lowest energy state functions have the highest concentration of electronic charge.

In the general case ψ_a and ψ_b will not have the same energies. As a result c_a and c_b will have different time coefficients and the state ψ will be said to "resonate" between ψ_a and ψ_b. This, however, must be considered carefully as the initial choice of ψ_a and ψ_b is usually somewhat arbitrary. The final result will be better the better the initial choice of functions is made.

MANY-DIMENSIONAL SPACE

Let us consider the case of two hydrogen atoms: two electrons and two protons. We can use the ideas of the last section only if we can express the Hamiltonian operator in useful form. In particular we wish to express the potential. This can be written

$$V = -\frac{q^2}{4\pi\epsilon_0}\left[\frac{1}{r_{aA}} + \frac{1}{r_{aB}} + \frac{1}{r_{bA}} + \frac{1}{r_{bB}} - \frac{1}{r_{ab}} - \frac{1}{r_{AB}}\right] \qquad (6\text{-}13)$$

Here r_{ij} is the distance between charge i and charge j. The subscripts a and b represent electrons, and A and B represent protons. This is not a good, simple spherical system for easy identification. We must be able to consider all possible combinations of the r_{ij}s. The means of doing this involves a multiple integration scheme for finding the expectation value. First, all particles but one are "fixed" momentarily and an integration is performed over all space for the one not fixed (e.g. the ith one). The variables of this integration could be considered as dr_i, $d\theta_i$, $d\phi_i$. The process is carried out N times for N total particles. As a result there are $3N$ space coordinates.

PROBLEMS

1. Show how, in the case of an H_2O molecule, the potential term in the Hamiltonian for an electron is a function of the unshielded portion of both of the two protons. Assume the proton-oxygen bonds are equally long and that they make an angle 2θ with each other.
2. In Fig. 6-1 both ψ_s and ψ_p are normalized. Why does ψ_s seem smaller than ψ_p over so much of the range? (Normalize ψ_s and ψ_p, i.e., evaluate c_{2s} and c_{2p}).
3. (a) Determine the directional characteristics of each of the three functions. (*Hint:* Note the nodal planes of the summed p states. Can the p functions be thought of as forming a rotated p function in a u, v, w coordinate system?)

$$\psi_1 = \frac{1}{\sqrt{3}}\left(\psi_{2s} + \sqrt{2}\,\psi_{2px}\right)$$

$$\psi_2 = \frac{1}{\sqrt{6}}\left(\sqrt{2}\,\psi_{2s} - \psi_{2px} + \sqrt{3}\,\psi_{2py}\right)$$

$$\psi_3 = \frac{1}{\sqrt{6}}\left(\sqrt{2}\,\psi_{2s} - \psi_{2px} - \sqrt{3}\,\psi_{2py}\right)$$

(b) With functions ψ_{2s}, ψ_{2px}, ψ_{2py} orthogonal and normalized, show that ψ_1, ψ_2, and ψ_3 are properly normalized.

4. Using the fact that $q\psi\psi^*$ is a charge density, determine the potential function of a free He^+ ion for an electron at any point in space. Express the results in integral form. Remember that the potential from the electron cloud has the opposite sign from that produced by the two protons in the nucleus. Naively this would seem to be the appropriate function for the second electron. Because of the symmetry, however, both electrons should have the same form for the potential. Thus the free He^+ ion with its ψ_{1s} electron is only a rough approximation to the true electron distribution when a second electron is to be considered. The neutral He atom must therefore be solved for by reiterative approximational means.

VII

CRYSTALS AND MODES

A dense cluster of atoms is said to be in a crystalline state when the atoms are arranged in an orderly way. Nearly all solids are crystals and the natural state of matter at low temperatures is crystalline, a clear indication that orderliness and low energy go together. The low energy of orderly systems is almost all due to the lower energy electronic states resulting from inter-actions of orderly systems, and these are the states that exist in solids. The atom cores have essentially the same energy whether the material is solid, liquid, or vapor at a given temperature. Thus it is the outer electronic states that are involved in determining structure. It is clear that structure itself can be considered an electronic property.

When atoms are not agitated greatly, that is, when the temperature is low, each atom can find the lowest energy relationship to its neighbors. This does *not* mean that the packing of atoms will be greatest, though in some cases this does occur. It does mean that atoms in silicon will have four nearest neighbor atoms instead of twelve as in copper. The arrangement of the neighbors is largely related to the degree of covalent bonding involved, the more covalent bonding, the fewer neighbors, and, to some extent, the more precisely they are positioned. Details of this are beyond the scope of this book.

Many of the physical properties due to the electronic states of a crystal can be deduced qualitatively by a very simple model in which identical atoms, each with one electron, are involved.

THE ONE-DIMENSIONAL CRYSTAL

The atoms in this very simple model are presumed to be spaced at equal intervals along a line. The distance between atoms is small enough so that the atomic eigenfunctions would overlap slightly, the spacing being about two or three times the hydrogen atom Bohr orbit diameter. At a distance corresponding to this interatomic spacing the charge density associated with the eigenfunctions of the free atom (i.e., the electronic function of an undeformed atom) would be such that 5 % of an atom's electronic charge would lie closer to the "wrong" atom. The eigenfunctions for the single isolated atoms could not be entirely correct here, however, because the potentials due to the charges of the neighboring atoms were not considered in the isolated case.

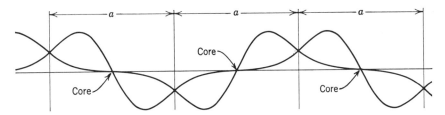

Fig. 7-1 The atoms are lined up and are slightly overlapping. The electronic state functions are assumed to be as in free atoms. Here the wave functions of neighboring atoms are shown 180° out of phase with each other.

Just as in the single atom, or in the potential wells discussed previously, a set of state functions should exist for the solid. These should be determined by the crystalline structure and, being state functions, should contain all the information about the system.

State functions can be formed by summing eigenfunctions. Even though the free atomic functions are not quite correct we use them, assuming that this is a reasonable first approximation. The two principal properties needed here are the overlap of eigenfunctions of adjacent atoms and the identical nature of all the atoms.

The overlap causes an interaction which gives a "springiness" to the system. One result of the springiness is that a disturbance produced at one point in the electronic system propagates down the line of atoms. Several facts are apparent from the identicalness of the atoms and eigenfunctions. The spatial dependence of each one is, of course, centered about a different core. This may be expressed in terms of $\phi_0(x)$, the spatial factor of the eigenfunction for the atom with nucleus at $x = 0$, and $\phi_n(x - na)$ the spatial factor of the nth atom's eigenfunction, where a is the interatomic spacing. Thus at some value of x_0 the 0th atom's state function ϕ_0 is just like the nth atom's state function at $x_0 + na$, excluding any phase factors, of course. The *time* relationship between neighboring atomic systems, for example the nth and $(n + 1)$th, must be independent of n. Otherwise more than a phase factor will be involved in translations from one atom site to another.

$$e^{-i\omega(t+\tau)}\phi_{n+1}(x - na - a) = e^{-i\omega t}\phi_n(x - na) \qquad (7\text{-}1)$$

where τ is independent of n.

For simplification of the mathematics, a new function $u(x)$ is defined. It is cyclic and has the property that

$$u(x) = u(x + a) \qquad (7\text{-}2)$$

Furthermore, in the "principal" range

$$\frac{a}{2} > x > -\frac{a}{2} \qquad (7\text{-}3)$$

we define

$$u(x) \equiv \phi_0(x) \qquad (7\text{-}4)$$

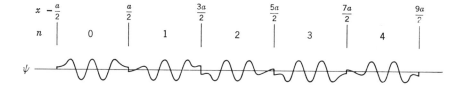

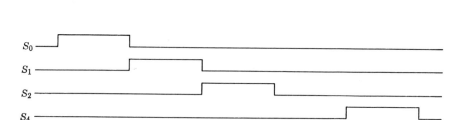

Fig. 7-2 Schematic of relevant functions.

By (7-4), u is defined in a "principal" range, and, by (7-2), in all other parts of space. It has a sort of "atomic" character by the "principle" range definition but repeats throughout the lattice (see Fig. 7-2). Then, from (7-1) to (7-4), for $n = 0$ (all terms being multiplied by $e^{i\omega\tau}$),

$$e^{-i\omega t}\phi_1(x - a) = e^{-i\omega t}e^{i\omega\tau}\phi_0(x) = u(x)e^{-i\omega t + i\omega\tau} = u(x - a)e^{-i\omega(t - \tau)} \quad (7\text{-}5)$$

Another factor is now introduced, $S_n(x) = 0$ for x *not* in the nth range $a(n + \frac{1}{2}) > x > a(n - \frac{1}{2})$, and $S_n(x) = 1$ when x *is* in this range (see Fig. 7-2). Then, by increasing n one at a time, we have

$$S_n(x - na)\phi_n(x - na)e^{-i\omega t} = S_n(x - na)u(x - na)e^{-i(\omega t - n\omega\tau)} \quad (7\text{-}6)$$

The $S_n(x)$ takes care of values of x not in the nth range. It states that the equality of relevance holds only in the nth range. One more step in notation before we construct the crystal state functions. A *variable* k is defined such that it relates the phase displacement and lattice spacing by

$$ak \equiv \omega\tau \quad (7\text{-}7)$$

Note that this k is not a constant, and, in particular, not Boltzmann's constant. It is used here because it is a standard symbol. It is a variable much as momentum is a variable. With this definition

$$S_n(x - na)\phi_n(x - na)e^{-i\omega t} = S_n(x - na)u(x - na)e^{-i(\omega t - kna)} \quad (7\text{-}8)$$

Note that ϕ_n is a function of k.

The interaction between atoms is due only to the overlap of the atomic functions. The entire structure of the crystal and all its crystalline properties thus depends on this overlap. But the use of S_n effectively removes *any* overlap. Since all interaction depends on overlap clearly neglecting it is a rather critical approximation. It is assumed, however, that all the important effects of the interaction are characterized in k (or τ). Therefore the dependence of various crystalline properties on k is to be determined remembering that k is related to the overlap interaction. Thus the overlap interaction is retained though the overlap itself is explicitly dropped. A more precise influence of overlap comes about by considering the interaction of *next nearest* neighbors. (See Brillouin, *Wave Propagation in Periodic Structures*, for an illuminating discussion of this subject.)

INTERACTIONS AND NORMAL MODES

In the investigation involving the interactions of many particles it is advantageous to look at their coordinated activity instead of trying to examine each particle alone in terms of its complicated environment. The interactions of electrons in solids, or in compounds having many electrons, are viewed most profitably in this way.

The basic ideas can be obtained by examining the very simple case of two identical pendulums interacting through a weightless spring. We assume small amplitudes of oscillation, where the restoring force on each is the sum of a term proportional to its displacement and a term proportional to the extension (or minus the compression) of the spring. The forces due to the spring are taken as zero when the pendulums are parallel. We therefore have two acceleration equations:

$$-m\frac{d^2x_1}{dt^2} = Cx_1 + G(x_1 - x_2)$$
$$-m\frac{d^2x_2}{dt^2} = Cx_2 - G(x_1 - x_2)$$

(7-9)

where x_1 and x_2 are the coordinates of the two pendulums. The spring-induced restoring forces must be equal and opposite, and, due to symmetry, both the C and G coefficients are the same in both equations (see Fig. 7-3).

When the two pendulums are swinging in parallel it is clear that the spring will have no effect and they will swing at the frequency of "free" pendulums. If they are symmetrical, both swinging toward each other at the same time (compressing the coupling spring), they reach the peak of their swings simultaneously and both then swing away from each other (thereby stretching the spring). In this mode their oscillations will be augmented by the spring and the oscillations will be more rapid. Let us describe the pendulum motions as "modes" M_1 (parallel) and M_2 (symmetric). Then

$$M_1 = \frac{x_1 + x_2}{2}$$
$$M_2 = \frac{x_1 - x_2}{2}$$

(7-10a)

We find

$$x_1 = M_1 + M_2$$
$$x_2 = M_1 - M_2$$

(7-10b)

It is clear that in the pure parallel case, where $x_1 = x_2$, M_2 is zero; and, when the pendulums are swinging in the perfectly symmetrical way described, $x_1 = -x_2$ so that $M_1 = 0$.

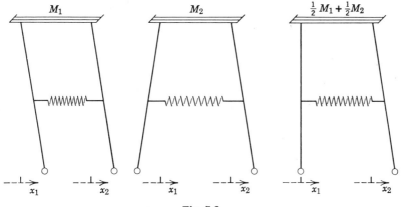

Fig. 7-3

Our differential equations can be put in terms of M_1 and M_2:

$$-m\left(\frac{d^2M_1}{dx^2} + \frac{d^2M_2}{dx^2}\right) = C(M_1 + M_2) + G(2M_2)$$

$$-m\left(\frac{d^2M_1}{dx^2} - \frac{d^2M_2}{dx^2}\right) = C(M_1 - M_2) - G(2M_2)$$

(7-11)

Adding and subtracting these two equations produces

$$m\frac{d^2M_1}{dx^2} = -CM_1$$

$$m\frac{d^2M_2}{dx^2} = -(C + 2G)M_2$$

(7-12)

Thus, where x_1 and x_2 result in two interacting equations, the two *modes* are not interacting. Each mode obeys a simple harmonic oscillation law:

$$M_1 = M_{10} \sin \omega_1 t$$

$$M_2 = M_{20} \sin \omega_2(t + t_0)$$

(7-13)

where $\omega_1 = \sqrt{C/m}$, $\omega_2 = \sqrt{(C + 2G)/m}$, and t_0 is a constant to be evaluated by the boundary conditions. Clearly the expressions for x_1 and x_2 are much more complicated. It can be shown easily that the two modes seem to have their own individual storage of energy. Each of the two modes can presumably oscillate independently of the other. Though it will not be shown here, they can be attenuated individually and each will then oscillate until its reservoir of energy is used up.

Modes will be identified with electronic state functions. Just as in the case of valence bonding, where everything could have been expressed in terms of sp^3 states, in the crystal we can express everything in terms of these modal states.

It should be particularly noted that M_1 and M_2 are defined by the phase relationship between pendulums one and two. Mode M_1 is an *in phase* mode, whereas M_2 is an *out of phase* mode. When more pendulums are involved, more modes are needed to describe the situation. They will be defined in terms of other phase relationships.

NORMAL MODES IN MANY-COMPONENT SYSTEMS

Some of the useful properties of normal modes are hidden by the two-component system of the example. It will be seen on studying the many-component system that the two-component system is a special case. The many-component systems, however, are the ones for which the normal mode technique is really important.

Consider a system of n identical pendulums, each linked to its neighbor by a weightless spring system.

Then, due to the indistinguishable nature of the pendulums, each of the differential equations of motion has the same form:

$$m \frac{d^2 x_n}{dt^2} = -C x_n + G(x_{n+1} - x_{n-1}) \qquad (7\text{-}13a)$$

Here, as before, each x is the displacement from the rest position of the pendulum designated by the subscript. The interdependence of each of the differential equations with those of the neighbors is clear. Now consider a

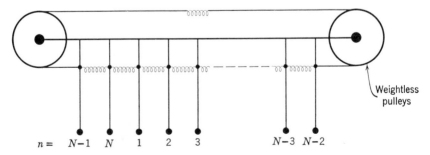

Weightless pulleys

$$n = \quad N{-}1 \quad N \quad 1 \quad 2 \quad 3 \qquad N{-}3 \quad N{-}2$$

Fig. 7-4 The many-pendulum system. Note that it is arbitrary which is called $n = 1$ because of symmetry.

normal mode system. Each x_n is expressed as a linear sum of normal modes, M_j:

$$x_n = \sum c_{nj} M_j \qquad (7\text{-}13b)$$

This is put into differential equation (7-13a) for x_n. M_j must satisfy

$$m \frac{d^2 M_j}{dt^2} = \left[-C + G \frac{c_{n+1,\,j} - c_{n-1,\,j}}{c_{nj}} \right] M_j \qquad (7\text{-}13c)$$

as this is the only basis for them to be normal (or orthogonal) and independent.

Equation (7-13c) can be obtained from each of the N equations of (7-13a), but to have any meaning it must be independent of which pendulum was used to obtain it, thus the factor $(c_{n+1,\,j} - c_{n-1,\,j})/c_{nj}$ is of necessity independent of n. This factor can be put in the form $(c_{n+1,\,j}/c_{nj}) - (c_{n-1,\,j}/c_{nj})$ and is independent of n; in fact it must be that $c_{n+1,\,j}/c_{nj} = c_{nj}/c_{n-1,\,j} = \gamma$. Note that γ is independent of n and that, if there are N pendulums in this symmetric system, the system is cyclic so that $x_n = x_{n+N}$, $c_{nj} = c_{n+N,\,j}$, and so on. Thus $\gamma^N = 1$ and $\gamma = 1^{1/N}$. In complex notation

$$\gamma = e^{2s\pi i/N} \qquad (7\text{-}13d)$$

where s is an integer. For the various M_js to be orthogonal, each must be associated with a different γ. There is a total of N *different* γs, one for each integral value of s, remembering that $\gamma_s = \gamma_{s+N}$. Note that the γs are equally spaced in " phase."

The x_ns are complicated functions of time whereas the M_js are all simple harmonic functions. Thus it is easier to comprehend situations when dealing with the M_js rather than with the x_ns. The values of c_{nj} of equation (7-13b) are determined by initially imposed conditions on the x_ns.

THE CRYSTALLINE STATE FUNCTION

Just as other state functions are formed by sums of eigenfunctions, a crystal state function is given by

$$\psi(x) = \sum_n c_n \phi_n(x) e^{-i\omega t} \qquad (7\text{-}14)$$

Such a system is difficult to work with and if the functions ϕ_n are to be the individual free atom eigenfunctions, they are not orthogonal. If we eliminate the overlap, the resulting approximate eigenfunctions $S_n \phi_n$ are orthogonal, however. Then, to simplify the situation greatly, we remove the overlap counting ϕ_n only when the nearest atom is the nth atom. Thus we write

$$\psi(x) = \sum_n c_n \phi_n(x) S_n(x) e^{-i\omega t}$$

Only one term in the summation is involved for each value of x due to the S_n. Using (7-6) and (7-2),

$$\psi(x) = \sum_n c_n u(x) S_n(x) e^{-i\omega(t-n\tau)}$$

$$= c_0 u(x) \sum_n S_n(x) e^{-i\omega(t-n\tau)} \tag{7-15}$$

The cs are to be taken as equal since the phase factor takes care of the only variation permitted between atoms. Thus, by substituting (7-7) in (7-15), we have

$$\psi(x, k) = c_0 e^{-i\omega t} u(x) \sum_n S_n(x) e^{ikan} \tag{7-16}$$

Note that ψ is a function of k, the atomic interaction parameter. At any particular value of x only one term of the sum contributed, specifically the S_n factors are nonoverlapping. In the nth range of x only e^{ikan} is involved and this changes stepwise to $e^{ika(n+1)}$ as x crosses into the $(n+1)$th range. Thus at $x = a(n + \frac{1}{2}) = a(\{n+1\} - \frac{1}{2})$ there will be a discontinuity in ψ. But discontinuities are not physically permissible. They can be avoided by a slightly different approximation. Let na be replaced by x, as though n were a continuous variable instead of a set of discrete integers. Then a simplification in form is possible, and, since only one term is contributing at a position, we have

$$\psi(x, k) = c_0 e^{-i(\omega t - kx)} u(x) \tag{7-17}$$

This form of state function is known as a Bloch function. Bloch functions have no discontinuities. The Bloch functions in three dimensions are among the most useful in studying the quantum mechanics of crystal properties.

Note that the state functions appropriate to the individual atoms have been summed and that the points of interest here will be the interaction modes. The Bloch functions are an approximation to the adding of individual atomic eigenfunctions and, in the region of an atomic core, the $u(x)$ factor has the properties of an atomic function. It will be easier to describe the overall situation in terms of these summed modes than in terms of the individual atoms, just as in the case of the pendulums. In the case of two pendulums the two modes summed were either in phase or diametrically out of phase. Two summed modes were then possible. Here, with tremendous numbers of atoms, the numbers of sums are almost infinite and they are expressed in terms of the phase between adjacent atom functions. Thus for each k, a different sum is involved, and, since the number of different sums is so large, k is essentially continuous and will be so treated.

In the following discussion, the earlier model with discontinuities (which we shall correct for in a different way) will be used, and the Schrödinger equation will be integrated by putting it in a difference equation form. Physically the difference equation approach effectively averages out small distances, thereby effectively removing the discontinuities by mathematical means rather than by a change of physical model. A look first at some properties and limits of k will be most instructive.

PHASE VELOCITY

For a moment consider just the real part of the state function $\psi(k)$. Its wave configuration is varying in time so that the wave appears to be traveling. If an observer moving with just the proper velocity could sense these functions, he would transfer his attention from one atomic function to the next at such intervals of time that it would appear to him that each of the eigenfunctions had the same constant phase. The wave configuration will thus seem to be constant to this observer. This can be the case only if $(kan - \omega t)$ is independent of time for him, that is, if n varies in his frame of reference such that

$$\frac{\partial}{\partial t}(kan - \omega t) = 0 = ka \left.\frac{\partial n}{\partial t}\right|_{cp} - \omega \qquad (7\text{-}18)$$

$$\left.\frac{\partial n}{\partial t}\right|_{cp} = \frac{\omega}{ka} \qquad (7\text{-}19)$$

The subscript cp indicates that the partial is taken at constant phase. Since the core spacing is a, a change in n of unity represents a change in x of a. Thus

$$a \left.\frac{\partial n}{\partial t}\right|_{cp} = \left.\frac{\partial x}{\partial t}\right|_{cp} = v_{cp} = \frac{\omega}{k} \qquad (7\text{-}20)$$

The velocity v_{cp} is known as the *phase* velocity and it is not unique. Compare two state functions which differ only in that $k_1 = -k_2$. It is at once apparent that the phase velocity of *one* is opposite that of *two*, that is, $v_{1cp} = -v_{2cp}$. Now compare two functions that differ in that $k_3 = k_1 + 2\pi r/a$ where r is an integer. Looking at equation (7-16), we see that

$$\psi(k_3) = c_0 e^{-i\omega t} u(x) \sum_n S_n e^{ian(k_1 + 2\pi r/a)} \qquad (7\text{-}21)$$

or

$$\psi(k_3) = c_0 e^{-i\omega t} u(x) \sum_n S_n e^{iank_1} e^{i2\pi rn} \qquad (7\text{-}22)$$

But clearly rn is an integer and the last exponential factor is unity. Thus $\psi(k_3) = \psi(k_1)$, and adding a multiple of $2\pi/a$ to k leaves ψ unchanged. Now let $k_1 = \pi/5a$, $r = -1$. Then $k_3 = \pi/5a - 2\pi/a = -9\pi/5a$. It is therefore seen that ψ can be represented as either a wave moving to the right with a phase velocity

$$\frac{\omega}{k_1} = \frac{5\omega a}{\pi}$$

or one moving to the left with phase velocity

$$\frac{\omega}{k_3} = \frac{-5\omega a}{9\pi}$$

Thus equation (7-16) is not unique in its interpretation. This can be visualized by an examination of a figure of vertically oscillating points (Fig. 7-15). *In a system of discrete points* only the motion of the points (or some other characteristic related to them) can be observed. The direction of the instantaneous vertical velocities of the points are shown in the figures by the small arrows.

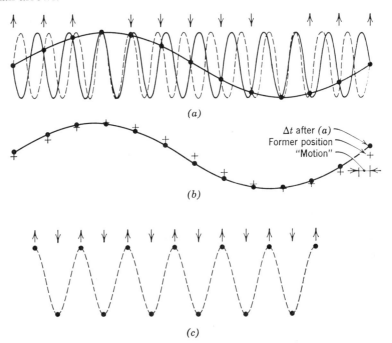

(a)

Δt after (a)
Former position
"Motion"

(b)

(c)

Fig. 7-5 Systems of discrete vertically oscillating points. Various possible phase velocity interpretations are illustrated.

An examination of Fig. 7-5 shows that the long wavelength "solid" wave and the short wavelength "dashed" wave must be visualized as moving to the left, whereas the short wavelength "solid" wave is clearly moving to the right (Fig. 7-5a). All three waves are visualized as representing the same identical motion of the points. In Fig. 7-5c the wave is not moving in either direction. It just sits and "pumps" up and down. In this particular case the wavelength is just $2a$.

Note that these concepts are largely due to the discrete nature of the "medium" in which the wave existed. However, they also apply to continuous systems of regularly spaced identical atoms. The waves there are the cyclic variations in the phases due to atomic interaction and, as shall be deduced by examining our special case, they are the probability amplitude waves of quantum mechanics.

Because of the cyclic behavior of k discussed above, all *real* information can be deduced by the examination of one cycle in k. Any full cycle will do. For convenience a *fundamental* period of k is chosen from which all solutions can be obtained. For reasons of symmetry let

$$\pi > ak > -\pi \qquad (7\text{-}23)$$

Before going further, the difference form of Schrödinger's equation, where V is taken as a constant, is needed. Now

$$-\frac{\hbar^2}{2m}\frac{\partial^2\psi}{\partial x^2} + V = -\frac{\hbar}{i}\frac{\partial\psi}{\partial t} \qquad (7\text{-}24)$$

In the discrete system a useful difference equation can be obtained by substituting:

$$\frac{\partial\psi}{\partial x}\bigg|_{n+1/2} \rightarrow \frac{\psi_{n+1} - \psi_n}{a} \qquad (7\text{-}25)$$

Here the subscript $n + \frac{1}{2}$ means the partial derivative at the point halfway between n and $n + 1$. The $\frac{1}{2}$ drops out in the next step. In a similar way,

$$\frac{\partial^2\psi}{\partial x^2}\bigg|_n = \frac{\partial}{\partial x}\frac{\partial\psi}{\partial x}\bigg|_n \rightarrow \frac{\dfrac{\partial\psi}{\partial x}\bigg|_{n+1/2} - \dfrac{\partial\psi}{\partial x}\bigg|_{n-1/2}}{a} \qquad (7\text{-}26)$$

or

$$\frac{\partial^2\psi}{\partial x^2}\bigg|_n \rightarrow \frac{\dfrac{\psi_{n+1} - \psi_n}{a} - \dfrac{\psi_n - \psi_{n-1}}{a}}{a} = \frac{\psi_{n+1} + \psi_{n-1} - 2\psi_n}{a^2} \qquad (7\text{-}27)$$

For the mathematical case $a \to 0$ the preceding "discrete system" representations become identical to the definitions of the derivatives. They clearly are correct only for cases where the ψ functions do not change appreciably in a distance a. From (7-24) and (7-23),

$$\frac{\hbar^2}{2ma^2}(\psi_{n+1} - 2\psi_n + \psi_{n-1}) + V\psi_n = \frac{\hbar}{i}\frac{\partial \psi}{\partial t} \tag{7-28}$$

Using the form for ψ given by (7-16), note that

$$\psi_{n+1} = \psi_n e^{ika} \qquad \text{and} \qquad \psi_{n-1} = \psi_n e^{-ika}$$

We obtain

$$\frac{1}{\hbar}V\psi_n + \frac{\hbar}{2ma^2}\psi_n(e^{ika} - 2 + e^{-ika}) = -\omega\psi_n \tag{7-29}$$

$$\frac{V}{\hbar} + \frac{\hbar}{2ma^2}(e^{ika/2} - e^{-ika/2})^2 = -\omega \tag{7-30}$$

From this, since $e^{iG} - e^{-iG} = 2i \sin G$,

$$\omega = \frac{2\hbar}{ma^2}\sin^2\frac{ka}{2} + \frac{V}{\hbar} \tag{7-31}$$

In Fig. 7-6, the energy is shown relative to a constant potential. The abscissa is proportional to k having been multiplied by a constant factor $\hbar$ as was ω in the ordinate. The product $\hbar k$ is known as the crystal momentum.

Equation (7-31) indicates that not all frequencies are possible, since $\sin^2 \theta$ normally has values between zero and one. Since $\hbar\omega$ is the energy, it is clear that not all energies are possible in this type of state function. Thus it is seen that the energies available to distributed states lie in a band. The states were formed by the superposition of essentially identical atomic states,

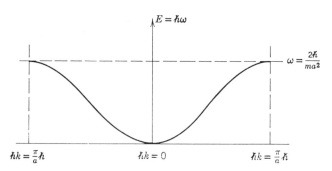

Fig. 7-6 Plot of energy versus crystal momentum.

only the phases of which differed. If the atomic states used are of the lowest energy, we obtain the so-called valence band of the solid. The electrons in this band are responsible for the binding of the atoms. If, instead of the ground state, excited states of each atom are used for superposition, other bands can be obtained. In the case of semiconductors one of these bands is known as the conduction band. Its lowest energy is above the highest energy of the valence band and thus there is a region of energy in which no distributed states can exist. The nature of the bands are discussed in somewhat more detail later.

NONLOCALIZED STATES

We have seen that in the lattice of discrete points (and presumably a lattice of atoms) only those states within specified energy ranges are nonlocal in the interaction of atomic functions. Higher or lower energies result in localized states. We also see that the frequency (and therefore energy $= \hbar\omega$) follows a strange relationship with the phase factor ka [equation (7-31)]. The allowed energies for nonlocalized states are called *energy bands*.

Recapitulating,

$$\psi(x, k) = c_0 e^{-i\omega t} u(x) \sum_n S_n e^{ikan} \tag{7-16}$$

It was shown that kx could be used instead of kan as an approximation. From this,

$$\psi(x, k) = c_0 e^{-i(\omega t - kx)} u(x) \tag{7-17}$$

or

$$\psi(x, k) = c_0 u(x) e^{-i\omega t} e^{2\pi i x/\lambda} \tag{7-32}$$

where the wave length λ is given by

$$\frac{2\pi}{\lambda} = k \tag{7-33}$$

For a *free particle* equation (2-15) can be written as

$$p = \frac{h}{\lambda} = \frac{2\pi\hbar}{\lambda} = k\hbar \tag{7-34}$$

The kinetic energy of a *free particle* is

$$E_{\text{kinetic}} = \frac{p^2}{2m} = \frac{2\pi^2\hbar^2}{\lambda^2 m} = \frac{k^2\hbar^2}{2m} = \hbar\omega \tag{7-35}$$

Thus, for a *free particle*,

$$\omega = \frac{k^2\hbar}{2m} \tag{7-36}$$

Let us examine our case in the energy band where ω does *not* obey the free particle relationship but rather obeys equation (7-31). In that equation a sine squared term enters. Trigonometric functions can be expanded in series so that, neglecting terms higher than the square, the trigonometric factor of equation (7-31) is given by

$$\sin^2 \frac{ak}{2} = \left(\frac{ak}{2} + \frac{a^3k^3}{48} + \ldots\right)^2 = \frac{a^2k^2}{4} + \ldots \tag{7-37}$$

Thus, *at low k values*, equation (7-31) reduces to

$$\omega = \frac{\hbar^2 a^2 k^2}{2ma^2} = \frac{\hbar k^2}{2m} \tag{7-38}$$

This is just the free particle relationship of equation (7-36). For large values of k, however, the deviation becomes great.

It should be noted that $E = \hbar\omega = \hbar^2 k^2/2m$ and therefore $\hbar k$ has one property of a momentum. The k is sometimes called the wave number vector (as, in a three-dimensional crystal, it has values dependent on direction and also gives the number of wave lengths per unit distance). The $\hbar k$ is sometimes called the "crystal momentum" (discussed further later).

The maximum ω of any one of this set takes place at $ka = \pi$ and here $\lambda = 2a$. This is just the wavelength that looks like a standing wave (see Fig. 7-5c) among discrete points which are spaced a apart. It is impossible in this case to state the wave's direction of motion. This is clear by examining the expression for ϕ. Subtracting 2π from ka leaves ϕ unchanged but reverses the interpreted wave direction and both values are in, or at the limits of, the fundamental period chosen.

COOPERATIVE EFFECTS AND "PARTICLES"

The results of adding eigenfunctions to obtain a state function have come up several times. It has, of course, been postulated that any state function could be expressed as a linear sum of eigenfunctions. Previously it was noted that this was of paramount importance in chemical and crystal bonding. In the case of bonding, though the charge distribution for a simple sp^3 state seemed to yield a spherical charge distribution, the cooperative effect caused the electrons' charge to be directionally dependent.

The probability of a particle being observed at some point is proportional to $\psi\psi^*$ at the point. Now we examine the motion of charge in solids. The eigenfunctions are spread throughout the crystal and therefore an individual eigenfunction can describe an electron not as a localized but only as a moving particle. When several eigenfunctions of nearly the same wavelength and frequency are added together, however, an effect is noted which can give the characteristics of a localized particle. As an example, two added sine waves are shown in Fig. 7-7. The regions of reinforcement have far higher $\psi^*\psi$ values than the regions of cancellation. The further addition of sine waves can give more localization and also the repetitive grouping can be reduced (the waves reinforce again further along beyond the cancellation). To remove this remote reinforcement a large number of states must cooperate. Mathematically this is handled by use of Fourier integrals. The results will be assumed. Here we will simply neglect the remote reinforcements. Now these waves are not static and therefore the regions of reinforcement move. The reinforcement regions correspond to particles in the sense that the particles are much more likely to be found there than elsewhere. The reinforcement group moves with what is known as a "group velocity," designated v_g.

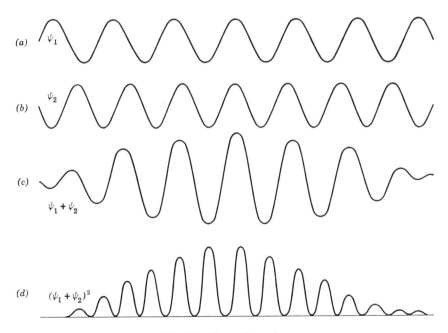

Fig. 7-7 Group formation.

The group velocity is calculated on the basis of the concepts of Fig. 7-6. The state function is proportional to the sum of two waves having slightly different wavelengths and frequencies, using the notation of (7-32), except letting $\nu = 2\pi\omega$:

$$\psi = cu\left[\exp 2\pi i\left(\frac{x}{\lambda_1} - \nu_1 t\right) + \exp 2\pi i\left(\frac{x}{\lambda_2} - \nu_2 t\right)\right] \quad (7\text{-}39)$$

or, by factoring,

$$\psi = cu\left\{\exp \pi i\left[x\left(\frac{1}{\lambda_1} + \frac{1}{\lambda_2}\right) - t(\nu_1 + \nu_2)\right]\right\}\left\{\exp \pi i\left[x\left(\frac{1}{\lambda_1} - \frac{1}{\lambda_2}\right) - t(\nu_1 - \nu_2)\right]\right.$$

$$\left. - \exp -\pi i\left[x\left(\frac{1}{\lambda_1} - \frac{1}{\lambda_2}\right) - t(\nu_1 - \nu_2)\right]\right\} \quad (7\text{-}40)$$

The second quantity in the curly brackets is just

$$2\cos \pi\left[x\left(\frac{1}{\lambda_1} - \frac{1}{\lambda_2}\right) - t(\nu_1 - \nu_2)\right] \quad (7\text{-}41)$$

Now we vary λ_1, to approach λ_2 (ν_1 also approaches ν_2). Then

$$\frac{1}{\lambda_1} + \frac{1}{\lambda_2} \to \frac{2}{\lambda} \quad \text{and} \quad \nu_1 + \nu_2 \to 2\nu$$

$$\quad (7\text{-}42)$$

$$\frac{1}{\lambda_1} - \frac{1}{\lambda_2} \to \Delta\left(\frac{1}{\lambda}\right) \quad \text{and} \quad \nu_1 - \nu_2 \to \Delta\nu$$

And

$$\psi = cu\left[\exp 2\pi i\left(\frac{x}{\lambda} - \nu t\right)\right]\cos \pi\left[x\Delta\left(\frac{1}{\lambda}\right) - t\,\Delta\nu\right] \quad (7\text{-}43)$$

The first factor is just like the original waves while the second is a modulating factor describing the wave's amplitude. We see that the modulating factor moves with a velocity which must be the group velocity:

$$v_g = \frac{\Delta\nu}{\Delta(1/\lambda)} \quad \text{or, in the limit,} \quad \frac{d\nu}{d(1/\lambda)} \quad (7\text{-}44)$$

The group velocity thus goes as

$$v_g = \frac{d\nu}{d(1/\lambda)} = \frac{(1/2\pi)d\omega}{(1/2\pi)dk} = \frac{d\omega}{dk} \quad (7\text{-}45)$$

The particle velocity, that is, the velocity of the region of reinforcement, is thus calculable when ω versus k is known. Now, from (7-31),

$$\omega = \frac{2\hbar}{ma^2} \sin^2 \frac{ak}{2}$$

Thus

$$v_g = \frac{2\hbar}{ma} \sin \frac{ak}{2} \cos \frac{ak}{2} = \frac{\hbar}{ma} \sin ak \tag{7-46}$$

The group (particle) velocity is therefore given by $v_g = \hbar k/m$ for k small. (Note that in this case the "momentum" $mv_g = \hbar k$.) For $ka \to \pi$, however, $v_g \to 0$. This is just what we observed in the eigenfunction of wavelength $\lambda = 2a$, which looked like a standing wave in the system of discrete points.

When the group concept is analyzed carefully, we find it has a limitation. If the levels are all occupied around the k value of interest, then the selection of one group automatically forces another group to be formed. The second group always describes electrons of opposite velocity. Thus in regions of densely occupied states the situation must be reviewed*.

In regions of k where the levels are only lightly occupied such automatic selections do not result and therefore the particle concept and group velocity are very well acceptable as is. This can, perhaps, be thought of more easily in terms of particles by thinking of an electron added to a system with lots of empty states. Due to applied electric fields, lattice disturbances, and so on, the electron does not "stay" in one state but bounces rapidly between many states very close together in energy and k. The electron is very unlikely to go, in fact, from one state to a second state if the second state does not have a large amplitude at the point of exchange. In other words, for a localized electron, the state of first occupancy must have a large ψ in the position where the electron is, and the second state must have its ψ large in that same region for the transition to take place. The electron, in fact, can be considered to bounce about only between states which reinforce one another at the position of the electron.

ACCELERATION OF ELECTRON IN AN ELECTRIC FIELD

When an electron moves in an electric field $\mathscr{E}$ its energy E changes by an amount

$$dE = -q\mathscr{E}\, dx = -q\mathscr{E}v_g\, dt \tag{7-47}$$

* Just as the atomic systems could be analyzed in terms of the sp^3 functions, so can the solid-state electronic system be analyzed in terms of these group functions. If all of the states are occupied in one orthogonal system they must also be in any other so that all the groups must be occupied.

where q is the absolute magnitude of the electron's charge and v_g its group velocity as before. But

$$v_g = \frac{d\omega}{dk} = \frac{\hbar}{\hbar} \frac{d\omega}{dk} = \frac{1}{\hbar} \frac{dE}{dk} \tag{7-48}$$

Thus, using (7-48) in (7-47),

$$dE = -q\mathscr{E}\left(\frac{1}{\hbar} \frac{dE}{dk}\right) dt \tag{7-49}$$

or, multiplying by $\hbar dk/dE$,

$$\hbar \, dk = -q\mathscr{E} \, dt \tag{7-50}$$

This should be compared with Newton's second law. One can show that in the classical case $dp/dt =$ force, or $dp =$ force x dt. This is known as an "impulse" equation as force x dt is an elemental impulse. We see that $\hbar k$, which we have suggested might be considered the electron momentum in the crystal, in fact changes with an impulse just as a momentum should.

Up to now we have been considering a linear crystal. The momentum, however, is a vector, so we expect k to be a vector (as $\hbar$ certainly is not). The limits of a principle region of k were set by the crystal spacing parameter a and this is generally directionally dependent.

In considering a one-dimensional crystal, note that dk/dt is independent of k. The crystal momentum increases uniformly in time until k reaches π/a. This point is indistinguishable from the situation for which $k = -\pi/a$. Thus, when the particle achieves a crystal momentum of $\hbar\pi/a$, it is reversed in direction. The "particle" reversal is not so sudden, even though the crystal momentum change is sudden. This is because v_g, the particle velocity, is always zero at this selection of the principal region boundary. The wavelength $\lambda = 2\pi/k$, so that when $k = \pi/a$ we have $\lambda = 2a$. Thus the wavelength associated here with the quantum mechanical particle is just what one would expect for some diffraction phenomenon. After the reversing diffraction occurs, the crystal momentum continues to increase at a constant rate. The sudden reversal accounts for just enough change in crystal momentum to make up for the gain in momentum over the entire period $2\pi\hbar/aq\mathscr{E}$ required for $\hbar k$ to go from $-\pi\hbar/a$ to $+\pi\hbar/a$. Thus, on the average, any group (or particle), if it passes through all possible states, will be as likely to have a momentum directed backward as forward and will be associated with one k value as much as with any other. This can be interpreted as a statement that the state density in k space is constant. Note especially that, if a band is filled, all k values are equally appropriate to groups and particles are going in one direction as much as in the opposite direction. Thus no conduction of current can take place. *Insulators* are materials which have filled bands only—no free electrons or partially filled bands.

The group velocity v_g changes with time proportional to the electric field too. It does not change at a constant rate, however, as the crystal momentum $\hbar k$ does. Starting at $v_g = 0$, first it increases in magnitude and then starts slowing down. From (7-46) and (7-50), we obtain

$$\frac{dv_g}{dt} = \frac{dk}{dt}\frac{dv_g}{dk} = -q\frac{\mathscr{E}}{m}(\cos ak) \qquad (7\text{-}51)$$

so that for values of k greater than $\pi/2a$ (only halfway to the limit of k in the case we have examined) the particle slows down as k increases further. This has been interpreted in various ways including a negative mass—which is inconsistent with the steady increase in momentum observed above. Actually, the situation is relatively complex in most cases in the region of the turning point. In some special and very important cases, however, simplification is possible. This is due to the invention of the "hole."

EFFECTIVE MASS

The electron group velocity is seen not to accelerate uniformly with an applied field. As its velocity changes, k, or $\hbar k$, also changes, and this, through the cosine factor, alters the acceleration.

Of principal interest is the "distorted" band. The interaction of atoms may be strong enough so that other than the nearest neighbors interact. In the real three-dimensional situation the nearest neighbors to a silicon atom are at four of the eight corners of a cube of which it is the center. The next nearest neighbors, of which there are twelve, are not in the same directions as the nearest neighbors and are only 1.63 times as far away. It is therefore not surprising that next nearest neighbor effects cannot be neglected. The effect of next nearest neighbors is to distort the k versus E relationship. A distortion of great interest is that frequently (in the case of both germanium and silicon) the minimum energy is *not* at $k = 0$. See Fig. 7-8, where A, B, and C are the positions of minimum energy (at $k = 0$, $k = 3\pi/4a$, and $k = \pi/a$).

This situation of a distorted band (whether or not the energy is minimum at $k = 0$) has several profound effects. One is that the electrons seem to have a mass other than the free mass. Equation (7-51) relates the acceleration, dv_g/dt, and the force on a charge, $-q\mathscr{E}$. The proportionality constant, $(\cos ak)/m$ in this case, can be obtained from $dv_g/d(\hbar k)$. The group velocity v_g itself was found in equation (7-48) as being $dE/d(\hbar k)$. Thus the effective

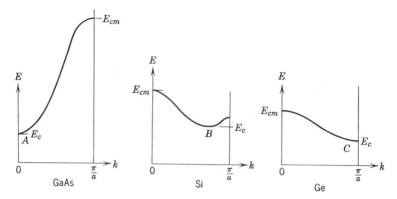

Fig. 7-8 E versus k (for k positive) for conduction bands. E_c, the bottom; and E_{cm}, the top of the conduction band are in each case. As stated before, k is a vector. In this figure the Si case is shown for k taken in the direction of a cube edge, whereas in the Ge case it is along a cube diagonal. The figure is spherically symmetric for GaAs near $k = 0$.

mass, which is $m/\cos ak = m_{eff}$ for the simple case of $k = 0$ at the bottom of the band, is more generally given as

$$\frac{1}{m_{eff}} = \frac{\partial^2 E}{\partial (\hbar k)^2} \tag{7-52}$$

The partial derivative is shown because of the vector character of k. The "effective mass" is defined by this and it is appropriate to use this expression at the minimum value of E such as at positions A, B, or C in Fig. 7-8. (Clearly m_{eff} is directionally dependent and, because two differentiations are involved, the components form a matrix which is symmetric because the order of differentiation is not important.)

The last several paragraphs have shown that $\hbar k$ behaves as a momentum, as a result of which it is known as the "crystal momentum." The atomic interaction factor k is then a vector quantity and is cyclic in that k and $k + 2\pi/a$ are physically indistinguishable. The number of crystal states or modes is constant in k. Thus there are as many crystal states with k in the range $-k_1 < k < -k_2$ as there are in the range $k_1 > k > k_2$. When a band is filled no electrical conduction can take place by virtue of that band. Thus insulators are materials with filled bands only. The dependence of energy on k is a function of both the atoms involved and the crystalline structure. Due to other than "nearest neighbor" interactions this dependence can be quite complicated. The "effective mass" is a parameter named because it takes the place of the classical mass in simple cases. However, it is a tensor quantity with six possibly different elements. "Average effective masses" are frequently employed, but the appropriate value depends on how it is to be used and the values for different purposes may be quite distinct.

THE HOLE

Heisenberg noted that when nearly all levels were occupied by electrons the situation could be described most easily by thinking of the few empty levels as though, instead of being empty, they were occupied by a positive charge, which, other than the sign of the charge, was similar to the electron. He called these positively charged concepts "defect electrons." All other levels were assumed empty of "defect electrons." The electrons were not, then, to be considered at all, but rather all their combined properties would be observable as though they were produced by the "defect electrons." Heisenberg's concept has proven very useful, particularly in the realm of semiconductors and insulators. We usually call the "defect electron" the "hole."

If we look at the hole as though it were a particle, we note that the occupancy of a lower energy level by a hole causes the electrons to take higher energy levels. Thus

low energy electron level = high energy hole level

To consider the system from the hole point of view, we must therefore also reverse our energy scale.

Then it is clear that as the hole moves in an electric field to *higher* energy *electron* levels, it should slow down as these are *lower* energy *hole* levels. If these high-energy electron levels are nearly filled with the electrons, they are only sparsely filled with holes. Then we can use the group velocity concept on the holes. The particle concept and group velocity concept are now consistent when the "hole" idea is adopted for the levels near the top of the band.

The groups are sums of energy eigenfunctions with nearly the same k value. Thus the group state function can be designated in terms of its center k value. Furthermore, the group has a momentum $\hbar k$. If all groups are occupied, the sum of their momenta must be zero because of the constant density of crystalline states in k:

$$\hbar \sum_n k_n = 0 \qquad (7\text{-}53)$$

If group i is not occupied but all the others are, the total momentum can be expressed as

$$\sum_{n \neq i} \hbar k_n = \sum_n \hbar k_n - \hbar k_i = -\hbar k_i \qquad (7\text{-}54)$$

Thus it is seen that the total momentum is just the negative of what the unoccupied group would have had if occupied. The total momentum can thus be thought of as the negative sum of momenta of unoccupied groups or we can reinvent the *hole*.

Because of the negative sign the effect of an electric field is the reverse of the effect on an electron and the hole behaves as a particle with *positive* charge and positive mass and obeys normal particle dynamics. In fact, the concept of holes is useful only in those regions where particle concepts are useful.

THE CONDUCTION PROCESS

The principal charge carriers have been introduced. The *groups* of modes act as the particles and each group can be assigned a value of crystal momentum $\hbar k$ and a velocity v_g. The crystal momentum changes at a uniform rate when an electric field is applied. We have already seen that, in spite of this, there is no net change in crystal momentum if the particle passes through the entire principal region as the diffraction process at $k = \pi/a$ reverses the direction of $\hbar k$. In the insulator this is the case since all states are occupied and the particle cannot transfer to another $\hbar k$ by a so-called *scattering process*. The *scattering processes* are basic to conduction. They are primarily due to atomic vibrational disorders. The vibrational disorders are known as phonons and they have energy $\hbar \omega$ and have momentum associated with them. They are thought to collide with groups and to transfer energy and momentum in the process. The group must then take on a new momentum and no new momenta are available in the insulator.

In the metal the Fermi level is well above the bottom of the band and well below the top. Thus the lower energy states are filled and the groups in them cannot be scattered by small amounts as all neighboring group states are occupied. Near the Fermi level many states are available to receive a scattered particle. In a three-dimensional crystal these available group states may have crystal momentum with only a slightly different orientation than that of the precollision particle. The change of direction thus, through many collisions, tends to rebalance the crystal momentum unbalance caused by an applied electric field. The collisions only partially succeed, so the momenta have a net unbalance due to the applied field.

In the semiconductor conduction band (valence band) most group states are empty (filled). The scattering process can then transfer a particle, an electron (a hole), from a group state with one k to almost any other. Thus the crystal momentum is unbalanced by an applied electric field only to the extent that the field changes the momentum between phonon collisions—because *after* the particle has been struck by a phonon (or itself strikes a crystal irregularity) it will have a random direction. The random post-collision direction is the result of random phonon directions and the general availability of group states with all $\hbar k$ values.

CONDUCTION AND VALENCE BANDS

Solids have their characteristic structure because of the low energy of the interacting electrons. Any alteration of atomic arrangement requires electronic state functions of substantially higher energy—and this energy must be supplied mechanically if forces are applied to stress the crystal. The hardness of a crystal is a measure of the extra electronic energy needed for a strained crystal.

In an insulator or semiconductor these structure-determining states have energies that make up the so-called "valence band." The individual atomic states that are interacting are the same ones that, in the separated atoms, determine its chemical valence—thus the name. The valence band in semiconductors is nearly full. If it were just full its electronic states could not enter into the conduction process and the material would be an insulator. If it is not quite full, that is, if the Fermi level is not above the band's top energy by too many kT, the conduction is best described by groups of unoccupied states or holes. Empty group states are near the "top" (positions of higher energy) of the band and therefore only the tops of nearly filled bands are of interest in conduction processes. The tops of such bands are designated with energy E_v.

In case there are only a few occupied states in a band they will best be described in terms of groups that have much of the character of free electrons. Such bands are known as "conduction bands" and only the energy versus k in the lowest energy range is normally of interest, as the particles will occupy the lower energy states according to Fermi statistics. The bottoms of such bands are designated by the energy E_c in semiconductor work. An energy gap of 20 to 50 kT exists between E_c and E_v in the useful temperature range of a semiconductor. No *nonlocalized* crystal states have eigenvalues of energy in this gap.

The conduction band can be thought of crudely as the interaction of atoms with excited-state electrons. The valence band on this simple construction was the result of ground-state interaction, where each interacting

atom was at its lowest energy. In the conduction band we could consider the
initial atom states as being in the first energy above the ground state, and
these excited systems then interact to produce the conduction band. The
excited states, in general, have larger radii of influence than the ground
states, as we have seen in the case of hydrogen. It is therefore to be expected
that the atoms will interact with their second nearest neighbors somewhat
more than they do when in the ground state. One result is that the conduction bands are frequently found to be more distorted from the "ideal"
band than is the valence band.

STATISTICS OF HOLES

In our studies of Fermi-Dirac statistics we found a way of expressing the
probability that a given state would be occupied. Because of the large
numbers of states involved this probability is also a good expression for the
fraction of the states in a given energy region that are occupied. The fraction
of states occupied is then expressible as

$$f = \frac{1}{1 + e^{(E - E_F)/kT}} \tag{7-55}$$

When $|E - E_F| \gg kT$, and $E > E_F$, this can be put in the form,

$$f_e = e^{(E_F - E)/kT} \tag{7-56}$$

or, for $E_F > E$,

$$f_h = 1 - f_e = e^{(E - E_F)/kT} \tag{7-57}$$

The two situations, (7-56) and (7-57), are useful in expressing the density
of levels occupied by electrons and holes, respectively. When these approximations are appropriate f_e or f_h is small and therefore the particle ideas hold.
When it is necessary to retain the form of (7-55) the levels are not sparsely
enough occupied to use the basic ideas of the "particle" electron or are too
empty to use the ideas behind the hole concept. As a result the system must
be treated entirely by quantum mechanics, the classical ideas of holes and
electrons not yielding results reliable enough for most purposes.

ELASTIC LATTICE WAVES: PHONONS

Atomic interaction in a crystal is, to a first approximation, elastic. Atoms
push and pull on each other with "Hookian" forces. Because of the uniform
spacing (in the atoms' rest positions) and because of their identical nature,

waves propagate very well in the crystalline material. A careful analysis of the situation leads to *the same equations that were evolved for electron crystal modes.* The details of the interactions are, of course, not the same; in particular, nearest neighbor atoms play an even more dominant role in the lattice atom vibration modes. Thus the systems for lattice vibrations are usually somewhat simpler.

Again grouping of modes takes a prominent place. The "particles" in this case are phonons—acoustic wave quanta in matter. These have appropriate k values over the same range, from $-\pi/a$ to $+\pi/a$, as the electron modes, and momenta again are given by $\hbar k$. They have energy $\hbar\omega$, as did the electron, and this is a function of the k and m appropriate to the group, again as in the electron case.

The masses of the vibrating atoms are, of course, very much greater than those of the atomic electrons. This makes the mass entering into equation (7-31) very much larger than in the electron case, and the ω thus is very much smaller.

Collisions between electrons and phonons take place with conservation of momentum and energy. The great difference of masses, however, makes the *energy interchange* between phonons and electrons very small on each collision so that energy transfer process is slow. After a collision each particle maintains very close to its old energy.

Momentum change, however, *can* be great at each collision in spite of this, because momentum is a vector quantity. Therefore the momentum can change direction without changing magnitude, and it is the square of its magnitude which is related to the particle energy. Although electron-phonon collisions can change the electron energy slightly (in terms of the energy range of the band) and can change the momentum drastically, they usually do not. Most electron-phonon collisions fall in the class of small angle collisions.

Another major distinction between the phonon and electron is the statistics each obeys. The phonons do not have a counterpart of the exclusion principle. Many phonons may be in identically the same phonon state. The phonon state, then, contributed an average energy $n\hbar\omega$ to the system. Here n is the probable number of occupants of the state. This probable number n is given by Einstein-Bose statistics; it looks very much like f of Fermi statistics:

$$n = \frac{1}{e^{\hbar\omega/kT} - 1} \tag{7-58}$$

Note the *minus* one as compared to the *plus* one of Fermi statistics. If $\hbar\omega$ is very small compared to kT, $e^{\hbar\omega/kT} = 1 + \hbar\omega/kT$ and equation (7-58) becomes very simple: $n = kT/\hbar\omega$, or, on the average, this mode has $n\hbar\omega$

or kT of energy. If n is small because $\hbar\omega \gg kT$, then $n = e^{-\hbar\omega/kT}$ and n *looks* very much like f, the *probabiltiy* of occupancy of electronic states in high energy situations. In these cases, $\hbar\omega \gg kT$, it is indeed just the probability of the phonon state being occupied.

When $\hbar\omega \gg kT$, then n is very, very small. Modes with high energy do not participate in this distribution of available energy. Only low-energy modes will share the energy and they share equally. This is the so-called "equipartition of energy" phenomenon.

Because of no Pauli exclusion principle for phonons, the lowest energy states can have the number of occupants changed at any time. Thus even at low temperature these states can be unoccupied or have multiple occupation. Furthermore, unlike charged particles where we have a conservation of charge and therefore a conservation of numbers of charged particles, there is no conservation of numbers of phonons. They can be *created* or *annihilated*. (Reducing temperature results in lots of annihilation.) The phonons are the major contributors to crystalline specific heat.

PROBLEMS

1. The energy in the coupled pendulum system is given by the sum of kinetic, gravitational potential, and spring potential energies. See Fig. 7-3. Thus

$$U = \tfrac{1}{2}[m(\dot{x}_1{}^2 + \dot{x}_2{}^2) + C(x_1{}^2 + x_2{}^2) + G(x_1 - x_2)^2]$$

Note that an $x_1 x_2$ term exists in the "spring" term. Show that energy U can be expressed in terms of M_1 and M_2 with *no* $M_1 M_2$ terms. Thus the modal "energy stores" are not linked.

2. Show that if $\dot{U} = 0$, that is, if U is constant in time, equations (7-9) and (7-12) can be derived.

3. Show that if the energy is dissipated by a "lossy" spring, that is,

$$\dot{U} = -k_1\left[\frac{d(x_1 - x_2)}{dt}\right]^2$$

only M_2 is damped. Show that a shock absorber put on the spring's center position such that

$$\dot{U} = -k_2\left[\frac{d(x_1 + x_2)}{dt}\right]^2$$

only M_1 is damped.

4. In the pendulum case the coupling was done by a mechanism that could store energy. Show that the circuit can be considered as two circuits coupled by C_2. What are the mode frequencies?

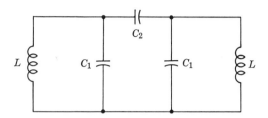

5. The coupling effect between atoms is described in terms of a parameter k. It is found that the characteristics change cyclicly as k increases. Show that in view of the definition of k in equation (7-7) this is entirely reasonable.

6. Three waves are shown in Fig. 7-5 for one set motion of points. Show how these specific waves can be fitted by the various criteria discussed for k and v_{cp}. Indicate specific values where possible. State in terms of "interatomic" parameter a, and so forth.

7. The group velocity v_g was defined in terms of the amplitude modulation cosine factor of equation (7-43). In the discussion leading up to that, and schematically in Fig. 7-7d the charge density (probability of finding an electron) is shown. Show the velocity, if any, of $(\psi_1 + \psi_2)^2$. Use the exponential form of equation (7-39). Compare this with the text.

8. A particular one-dimensional crystal has interactions such that

$$\omega = \frac{2\hbar}{ma^2}\left(\sin^2\frac{ak}{2} + \frac{1}{2}\sin ak\right)$$

Plot energy versus k for this system. What is the value of k for minimum energy? What is the effective mass at the minimum energy point? What is the crystal momentum at the minimum energy point?

9. What are the values of the electrons v_gs in the conduction bands? The situations are as depicted in Fig. 7-8 for $k = 0$ and for k such that the electrons are at E_c. What are the crystal momenta for these electrons?

10. In light of equation (7-54) regarding the momentum associated with a nearly filled band, show how the momentum for *holes* changes with an applied field, note equations (7-47) through (7-50). Use v_{gh}, and so on, in your notation. Is your result consistent with the electron formulation?

11. Consider equation (7-53). In the crystal ak_n is the phase difference between atomic wave functions that make up the modes, a being the interatomic spacing. Now examine the many-pendulum system of Fig. 7-2. What corresponds to ak_n? Show that equation (7-53) holds in the many-pendulum case also.

12. Draw suitable energy and momentum diagrams for an electron-phonon collision. Consider case (a), the momentum can be only in one dimension and case (b), the momentum can be in two dimensions.

VIII

TRANSITIONS
AND EIGENFUNCTIONS

In "real" situations it is usually very difficult if not impossible to solve quantum mechanical equations. It is therefore important that we in fact do not need the eigenfunctions at all in some instances and in all other situations we can make very good approximations to the eigenvalues with only rough approximations to eigenfunctions. It is also possible using somewhat parallel means to make partial corrections to the eigenfunctions (though we will not do this here).

We have emphasized the stationary states. In fact much experimental work involves the transitions *between* stationary states. If we want to know how hard something is, we measure the difficulty of deforming it. A black object absorbs light energy because its electrons make transitions to higher levels. Thus, although we must understand the stationary state, our work would be incomplete without some introduction to transitions between stationary states.

EIGENVALUES WITHOUT EIGENFUNCTIONS: COMMUTATION

Thus far in this book it has been implicit that it was necessary to find the solution to the operator equation. That is, the eigenfunctions had to be determined to obtain the eigenvalues. It is therefore somewhat surprising that some of the *properties* of functions and operators can be used to find eigenvalues without finding the eigenfunctions. This is the case, for example, for angular momenta. Because of lack of commutation among the angular momentum operators and because they are Hermitian, angular momentum eigenvalues can be obtained without knowledge of the eigenfunctions.

In classical mechanics, angular momentum is a vector product of the radius vector and the linear momentum.

$$\mathbf{M} = \mathbf{r} \times \mathbf{p} \tag{8-1}$$

The components are, in cyclic form,

$$M_x = y p_z - z p_y \tag{8-2}$$

$$M_y = z p_x - x p_z \tag{8-3}$$

$$M_z = x p_y - y p_x \tag{8-4}$$

Then the quantum mechanical operators are obtained by direct substitution. It is readily shown (see Problem 8-1) that

$$\hat{M}_x \hat{M}_y - \hat{M}_y \hat{M}_x = -\frac{\hbar}{i} \hat{M}_z = i\hbar \hat{M}_z \tag{8-5}$$

$$\hat{M}_y \hat{M}_z - \hat{M}_z \hat{M}_y = -\frac{\hbar}{i} \hat{M}_x = i\hbar \hat{M}_x \tag{8-6}$$

$$\hat{M}_z \hat{M}_x - \hat{M}_x \hat{M}_z = -\frac{\hbar}{i} \hat{M}_y = i\hbar \hat{M}_y \tag{8-7}$$

It is also easily demonstrated (see Problem 8-2) that

$$\hat{M}^2 (= \hat{M}_x{}^2 + \hat{M}_y{}^2 + \hat{M}_z{}^2)$$

commutes with each of the component operators:

$$\hat{M}^2 \hat{M}_z - \hat{M}_z \hat{M}^2 = 0 \tag{8-8}$$

Some so-called "shift" operators exist. To see the meaning of "shift" let us examine $\hat{M}_x + i\hat{M}_y$, which is one of them. From (8-6) and (8-7),

$$\hat{M}_z(\hat{M}_x + i\hat{M}_y) - (\hat{M}_x + i\hat{M}_y)\hat{M}_z = +i\hbar \hat{M}_y + \hbar \hat{M}_x = +\hbar(\hat{M}_x + i\hat{M}_y) \tag{8-9}$$

or

$$\hat{M}_z(\hat{M}_x + i\hat{M}_y) = (\hat{M}_x + i\hat{M}_y)(\hat{M}_z + \hbar) \tag{8-10}$$

Similarly,

$$\hat{M}_z(\hat{M}_x - i\hat{M}_y) = (\hat{M}_x - i\hat{M}_y)(\hat{M}_z - \hbar) \tag{8-11}$$

Now assume that Y_{1m} is an eigenfunction of $\hat{M}_z$ with eigenvalue k_e. Then

$$\hat{M}_z Y_{1m} = k_e Y_{1m} \tag{8-12}$$

Using (8-10), we find

$$\hat{M}_z(\hat{M}_x + i\hat{M}_y)Y_{1m} = (\hat{M}_x + i\hat{M}_y)(\hat{M}_z + \hbar)Y_{1m} = (\hat{M}_x + i\hat{M}_y)(k_e + \hbar)Y_{1m}$$
$$= (k_e + \hbar)(\hat{M}_x + i\hat{M}_y)Y_{1m} \qquad (8\text{-}13)$$

Note that this is of the form

$$\hat{M}_z[(\hat{M}_x + i\hat{M}_y)Y_{1m}] = (k_e + \hbar)[(\hat{M}_x + i\hat{M}_y)Y_{1m}] \qquad (8\text{-}14)$$

Thus when Y_{1m} is an eigenfunction of $\hat{M}_z$, the quantity in square brackets is also an eigenfunction of $\hat{M}_z$ and its eigenvalue is $\hbar$ greater. Thus the designation "shift operator": it produces new eigenfunctions and stepped-up eigenvalues.

By symmetry all angular momentum eigenvalues can be deduced without ever knowing Y_{1m}.

AN APPROXIMATIONAL METHOD: FIRST-ORDER
PERTURBATION THEORY

Suppose we have a system that is not simple but is only slightly different from a simple system for which we know the answers. For example, let us examine a particle in a potential well such as Fig. 8-1a. Compare this with

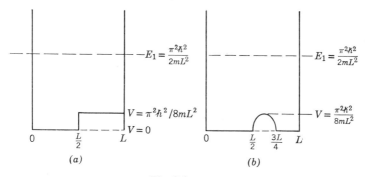

$$-E_1 = \frac{\pi^2\hbar^2}{2mL^2} \qquad -E_1 = \frac{\pi^2\hbar^2}{2mL^2}$$

$$V = \pi^2\hbar^2/8mL^2 \qquad V = \frac{\pi^2\hbar^2}{8mL^2}$$

$$V = 0$$

(a)   (b)

Fig. 8-1

Fig. 3-2. The dashed lines here show the potential and the eigenvalue E_1 for the Fig. 3-2 situation. In the new situation the potential is said to be "perturbed" or to be a "perturbation of" the old potential. Now in this particular perturbation we could, with a little more work, compute the correct eigenfunctions. But suppose the potential had been as in Fig. 8-1b. This would be a great deal more difficult, if not impossible, to calculate analytically by standard means. Ideas relative to perturbation theory have been used in astronomy to calculate third-body effects on orbits, but in systems with discrete states it was apparently introduced by Lord Raleigh to the field of acoustical resonance. Schrödinger modified the theory for use in quantum mechanics.

In the perturbation theory of quantum mechanics an estimate of the energy can be made without knowledge of how the eigenfunction is modified. The following technique is available for repetitive steps. In order to make the first-order correction to the eigenvalue, no correction to the eigenfunction is needed, but a means of first-order correction to the eigenfunction is also available following which a second-order eigenvalue correction can be made. Here we will use a simpler system which only yields a first-order eigenvalue correction.

From the mean value theorem an exact energy for a system is given by

$$\langle E \rangle = \int \psi^* \hat{H} \psi \, d\tau \tag{8-15}$$

Here ψ must be known. If we assume that $\hat{H}$ is very much like $\hat{H}_0$ and that $\hat{H}_0$ has eigenfunctions ψ_n, it is reasonable to assume that ψ is very much like one of the eigenfunctions ψ_n. Let us assume that we are interested in the ground level of energy and that ψ is then nearly like ψ_0. Expand ψ in terms of ψ_ns:

$$\psi = \sum a_n \psi_n \tag{8-16}$$

where a_0 is large and all other a_ns are small. Let $\hat{H}_1$ be the perturbation of $\hat{H}_0$ as depicted in Fig. 8-1a as an irregularity of the potential. Then

$$\hat{H} = \hat{H}_0 + \hat{H}_1 \tag{8-17}$$

and

$$\hat{H}_0 \psi_n = E_{0n} \psi_n \tag{8-18}$$

Then

$$\langle E \rangle = \int \left(\sum a_m^* \psi_m^* \right) \left(\sum a_n E_{0n} \psi_n + \sum a_n \hat{H}_1 \psi_n \right) d\tau \tag{8-19}$$

$$\langle E \rangle = a_0^* a_0 E_{00} \int \psi_0^* \psi_0 \, d\tau + a_0^* a_0 \int \psi_0^* \hat{H}_1 \psi_0 \, d\tau + (0) \tag{8-20}$$

Here (0) represents terms in $\hat{H}_1$ and/or a_n^*, $n \neq 0$. The integrals with no $\hat{H}_1$ in them are explicitly zero if $m \neq n$ and the ψs are orthogonal. The effect of $\hat{H}_1$ is assumed small so that integrals involving it are small if $m \neq n$ and the coefficients are small in any case if $m \neq 0$, $n \neq 0$. Thus as a first-order correction we neglect (0) and, in fact, estimate $a_0^* a_0$ at being unity. Thus we have simply

$$\langle E \rangle = E_{00} + \int \psi_0^* \hat{H}_1 \psi_0 \, d\tau \qquad (8\text{-}21)$$

Hence an energy correction is made without specific knowledge of the new wave function. Frequently the evaluation of the integral must be done numerically. Only the real portion of the integral is of physical significance. If a set of eigenfunctions exist that correspond to $\hat{H}_1$, then the preceding integral is real.

As an example of this procedure let us find E for the ground state of the system of Fig. 8-1a. Now E_{00} is given in the figure and ψ_0 is real and is given in Chapter III as $\sqrt{2/L} \sin \pi x/L$. $\hat{H}_1$ can have any finite assigned values outside the region $L > x > 0$ and, in the range $L/2 > x > 0$ it is zero while in the range $L > x > L/2$ it is simply $V_1 = \pi^2 \hbar^2 / 8mL^2$. The derivative operator portion of $\hat{H}$ is just like that of $\hat{H}_0$ and therefore $\hat{H}_1$ is a simple multiplier here:

$$\int \psi_0^* \hat{H}_1 \psi_0 \, d\tau = \frac{\pi^2 \hbar^2}{8mL^2} \int_{L/2}^{L} \psi_0^* \psi_0 \, dx \qquad (8\text{-}22)$$

$$= \frac{\pi^2 \hbar^2}{8mL^2} \frac{2}{L} \int_{L/2}^{L} \sin^2 \frac{\pi x}{L} \, dx = \frac{\pi^2 \hbar^2}{8mL^2} \frac{2}{L} \frac{L}{4} = \frac{\pi^2 \hbar^2}{16mL^2} \qquad (8\text{-}23)$$

Thus the first-order correction of $\langle E \rangle$ gives

$$\langle E \rangle = E_{00} + \frac{\pi^2 \hbar^2}{16mL^2} = \frac{9\pi^2 \hbar^2}{16mL^2} \qquad (8\text{-}24)$$

Note that the result might well have been arrived at intuitively. The "intuitive" response to the irregularity might have been: "smooth it out." This would have given the same result since the extra energy is just the average increase in the potential energy. However, the result of analysis of the situation depicted in Fig. 8-1b will not lead to such a simple result except at certain excited levels.

SPATIALLY ATTENUATED STATES

In such regular structures as crystals or large organic molecules the concept of bands is very useful. At the ends of or at any point along a long chain molecule where there is a deviation from regularity (such as an extra hydrogen proton attached to one of the carbon atoms) the electronic states must deviate from that of the otherwise regular system. Some of these deviations can be handled by perturbation theory, others by modified boundary conditions. But it yields much more insight if these are examined

TRANSITIONS AND EIGENFUNCTIONS

for the localization or trapping of electrons by a charged "impurity" in a semiconductor or by an appended proton (hydrogen core) on an organic molecule chain, or for electrons *penetrating* barriers. In this latter situation we had previously noted (see, e.g., Fig. 5-1) that electronic wave functions, and therefore effective charge density, may exist where the total energy is less than the potential energy alone. One result of the investigation will show why electrons may penetrate thin regions even though classically they would be reflected. The examples are taken from the field of semiconductors where two problems arise which require some modifications of band concepts.

1. *Trapping* of electrons implies that the electrons are held locally somehow and that it takes added energy to put them into the bands where they are not localized. As a result so-called "impurity levels" are shown in the energy gap below the conduction band for electrons and above the valence band for holes (see Fig. 8-2a). The electrons in states having these levels are attracted to and held by charged ionic cores and thereby "localized." What is the nature of the wave functions for these localized electrons? We will

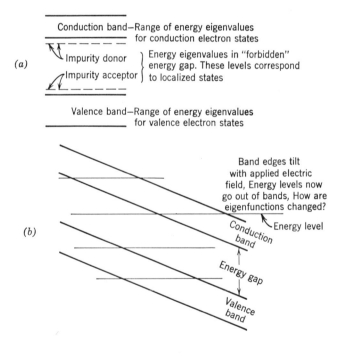

Fig 8-2

examine this by investigating the nature of wave functions at energies not allowed in the bands.

2. When electric fields are applied, the band edges are shown tilted (see Fig. 8-2b). This does not seem unreasonable since the entire potential is modified by the applied voltage. A potential energy, linear with distance, is added to the energy picture. Energy levels, however, are *level* (not tilted). Thus the energy corresponding to the appropriate eigenfunction extends into the so-called "gap." What is the nature of the wave function in this region from which they are normally excluded?

Both of these cases have in common that the energy is outside the bounds set by the previous considerations.

For the previously examined solutions $\omega \leq 2\hbar/ma^2$, for $V = 0$. Let us now examine the case involving somewhat higher energy:

$$\hbar\omega > \frac{2\hbar^2}{ma^2} \tag{8-25}$$

Here, then, ω is taken as greater than for the case where $\sin ak/2 = 1$, but, from (7-31), this equality "obviously" yields maximum ω. Does it really? If ω is slightly greater than the maximum band value previously calculated, it can be put in the form

$$\omega = \frac{2\hbar}{ma^2}(1 + 2\varepsilon) = \frac{2\hbar}{ma^2}\sin^2\left(\frac{ka}{2}\right) \tag{8-26}$$

It is still assumed that (7-31) holds, but, in view of remarks in Chapter I, it is clear that k must be a complex quantity. In equation (8-26) the ε is taken as real and $1 \gg \varepsilon > 0$. From this we see that

$$\hbar\omega = \frac{2\hbar^2}{ma^2} + 2\varepsilon\left(\frac{2\hbar^2}{ma^2}\right) = (KE)_{\max} + 2\varepsilon(KE)_{\max} \tag{8-27}$$

This can be written as

$$\hbar\omega - (KE)_{\max} = \Delta E = 2\varepsilon(KE)_{\max} \tag{8-28}$$

ΔE being the excess of energy over the band maximum. In terms of energy, then,

$$2\varepsilon = \frac{\Delta E}{(KE)_{\max}} \tag{8-29}$$

where $(KE)_{\max}$ is the "maximum" value of the kinetic energy in the band. Then

$$\sin\frac{ak}{2} = \sqrt{1 + 2\varepsilon} = 1 + \varepsilon \tag{8-30}$$

This is possible only if the argument $ak/2$ of the sine function is complex as before mentioned. To see this, let

$$\tfrac{1}{2}ak = \alpha + i\beta \qquad (8\text{-}31)$$

both α and β being real and α is greater than zero. It then follows, by a trigonometric identity, that

$$\sin\frac{ak}{2} = \sin(\alpha + i\beta) = \sin\alpha\cos i\beta + \cos\alpha\sin i\beta \qquad (8\text{-}32)$$

But imaginary arguments of trigonometric functions turn them into hyperbolic functions with real arguments, and these can become very large, just what we were seeking. Thus

$$\sin\frac{ak}{2} = 1 + \varepsilon = \sin\alpha\cosh\beta + i\cos\alpha\sinh\beta \qquad (8\text{-}33)$$

Since $1 + \varepsilon$ is real, the second term on the right must be zero, therefore we must have $\cos\alpha = 0$ as $\beta \neq 0$. From this

$$\sin\alpha = 1 \qquad (8\text{-}34)$$

thus $\alpha = \pi/2$. Then (8-33) reduces to

$$1 + \varepsilon = \cosh\beta = 1 + \frac{\beta^2}{2} + \frac{\beta^4}{24} + \qquad (8\text{-}35)$$

where we can drop the higher order terms as β is given as small. From this we see

$$\beta = \pm\sqrt{2\varepsilon}, \qquad ak = 2\left(\frac{\pi}{2} \pm i\sqrt{2\varepsilon}\right) \qquad (8\text{-}36)$$

and

$$ak = \pi \pm 2i\sqrt{2\varepsilon} = \pi \pm 2i\sqrt{\frac{\Delta E}{(KE)_{\text{max}}}} \qquad (8\text{-}37)$$

The atomic interaction parameter k thus is seen here to be a complex quantity. For $\omega > \omega_{\text{max}}$, we then see from (7-16) that an $i \cdot i$ develops in the exponent:

$$\phi(k) = c_0 u(x)e^{i\omega t}\sum_n\left(\exp \pm 2n\sqrt{\frac{\Delta E}{(KE)_{\text{max}}}}\right)S_n e^{in\pi} \qquad (8\text{-}38)$$

This has, we shall see, a very strong localizing factor due to the *real* exponent. This is more apparent if x/a is put in place of n. Then the *real* exponent enters as

$$\exp\left(\pm 2\,\frac{x}{a}\sqrt{\frac{\Delta E}{(KE)_{\max}}}\right) \tag{8-39}$$

A positive or negative coefficient is chosen to keep the ϕ function finite. The eigenfunction would become infinite if the positive sign in the exponent were used for the region $x > 0$. Thus for $x > 0$ the negative sign in the exponential must be used and the positive sign is useful only for the region $x < 0$ (n going toward negative infinity). Therefore the real portion of the exponential shows a decay in both directions from what must be considered to be some potential minimum point. These localized states are produced by impurities. The degree of localization depends on the energy separation, ΔE, from the band. Very similar results are obtained for the case of E less than $E_{\min}$. When the localized state is above the band it is usually an "acceptor" level and when it is below the band it is usually a "donor" level (see Fig. 8-3).

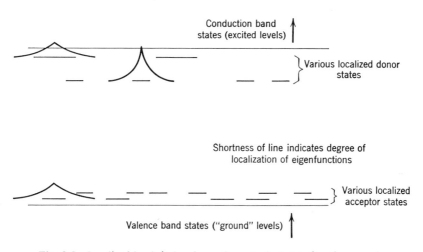

Fig. 8-3 Localized levels in band gap. Some typical state functions are shown.

In three dimensions the localization would be seen to be spherically symmetric; it would in fact be just the form produced by a positive charge which could attract electrons (or a negative charge that could attract holes). The wave functions might then be called "hydrogenic," although they will be much larger in linear dimensions and the "trapped" electron will be spread out over the volume occupied by many atoms of the crystal. The trapped electron is not *very* localized and its charge is said to be diffuse.

TRANSITIONS AND TUNNELING

The band type eigenfunctions previously calculated are not strictly appropriate to the case of the tilted bands. The tilt, due to the potential energy variation produced by the applied electric field, causes levels of energy (of whatever eigenfunction) to extend into the energy gap between bands as shown in Fig. 8-4. The "tilted" region between bands is given by

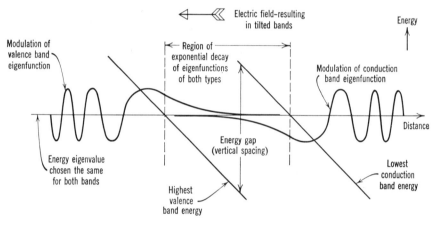

Fig. 8-4

the energy gap divided by the electric field strength. The field, as shown here, is uniform. For tunneling to be important this region should not be greater than about 100 Å.

The band type wave functions are shown, even if somewhat inappropriate, for two reasons: first, they are fairly useful if the applied field does not change the potential very much per atomic spacing; and second, we know what they are and how they vary when their energy is outside the ordinarily imposed band limits. When the potential does not change much in an atomic spacing it is not unreasonable to use the band potential as though it were a constant and to use the corresponding eigenfunction as though it applied in that local region. In effect we are then using a slowly varying potential where our solution was for a constant one.

In the energy gap the field is high but it still does not change the potential markedly between atoms. We use the real exponent of equation (8-39); however, ΔE will now be linear with distance:

$$\Delta E = \frac{E_g}{W} x \qquad (8\text{-}40)$$

where W is the width of the high field region and E_g is the energy gap. Thus the eigenfunction has an exponential of the form

$$\exp\left[\pm 2\,\frac{x}{a}\sqrt{\frac{xE_g}{W(KE)_{max}}} \right] \qquad (8\text{-}41)$$

The narrower the gap, the larger the exponential. But x has a maximum value of W so that in fact the maximum magnitude of exponent goes as $W\sqrt{E_g/(KE)_{max}}$. The width W is determined almost entirely by the impurity concentration gradients produced during fabrication of the diode.

Figure 8-4 shows a situation where two state functions, "tails" of the valence band and conduction band states, have the same energy and coexist in the same volume (they overlap largely in the tilted band gap). If the tails are sizeable, it indicates that the electrons can be found in the gap region. Such indicated overlap indicates further that an electron may transfer from one of these states to the other, transferring from a valence band state to a conduction band state, thus "tunneling" from the valence band to the conduction band, or vice versa. This transition from one state to another is a more precise interpretation of the barrier penetration of Chapter III. The two states are different and probably involve, for example, different momenta. Thus any transition mechanism must have means for conserving the momentum. This particular tunneling is known as Zener tunneling and is the basis for the Esaki or tunnel diode. In this diode, transitions between valence and conduction bands permit large currents to flow. The needed overlap for the transitions is greatest if the spatial extent of the exponential decay is least. A large electric field tilts the bands more, thus providing a shorter "tunneling" distance.

The transition probability is great for a large overlap. But the states are pseudo stationary and this precludes transitions unless a disturbance takes place. Actually disturbances are plentiful, but in this case the disturbing entity may have to supply (or be able to remove) any momentum difference bewteen valence and conduction band states. Phonons are the common disturber and are especially important when in the neighborhood of an impurity atom. A high density of impurity atoms is always present in these high electric field Esaki diode cases, so the situation is just right.

CONDUCTIVITY AND TRANSITIONS

We have found that crystal momentum is modified by the electric field in such a way that the electrons increase their momentum. This should solve the problem of conductivity. However, the electron has a changing effective mass and the group velocity may *decrease* rather than increase with increasing momentum. We would then have the case of a negative resistance if this were a usual event. Furthermore, as the crystal momentum continues to increase under the influence of the electric field, the velocity might even *reverse*. This is clearly just a recapitulation of our previous arguments that the wave functions are cyclic in k.

This mental obstacle breaks down when transitions between states are considered. If the electron is initially accelerated from a low energy position (where most particles are) it will be far above the initial low energy position before its acceleration as a free (group) particle stops. Long before this it will suffer a transition to a lower energy state and start accelerating all over again. Thus the usual conductivity situation involves many transitions between states with acceleration starting all over after each one. The regions of very high crystal momentum, where v_g might in fact reverse, are essentially avoided. Note that the loss of energy in the transitions is known as I^2R loss.

OPTICAL TRANSITIONS

Quantum mechanics, as originally formulated, was developed mostly to explain optical phenomena. Light absorption and emission are today of great "engineering" interest both because of chemical effects and application to lasers.

When an electron in some crystal state absorbs a light photon its energy is raised by $h\nu$, (or $\hbar\omega$). The electron has an initial momentum (a vector) of $\hbar\mathbf{k}$, say, while the photon has an initial momentum $h(1/\lambda)$. The reciprocal wavelength is known as the "wave number" and is a vector with a direction the same as that of propagation. The absorption of the photon must not only conserve energy but must also conserve momentum. Now k, as has been seen, has a maximum meaningful value of π/a. Thus $\hbar\pi/a = h/2a$ is the maximum value of the carrier momentum. Now a is perhaps 4 Å, whereas λ, for "light," is in the neighborhood of 4000 Å. Thus the momentum associated with the light is almost negligible compared to the momentum of the carrier.

As an approximation, good in many cases, light-induced electronic transitions in solids are adequately described in terms of change in *energy only*, with *no* change in momentum. Specifically this means that optical transitions in solids can occur only between states of the same momentum—unless a phonon is also involved. There is a notable exception: when two states at different energies have identical momentum, such as the 1*s* and 2*s* states of an atom where each has zero momentum. In this case the photon momentum, although small, upsets things and the transition is impossible because the photon momentum is not precisely zero.

Transitions where an electron drops from a level of one band to a level in another band must conserve both energy and momentum. Consider the case of GaAs in Fig. 8-5. In this case the lowest energy electrons in the con-

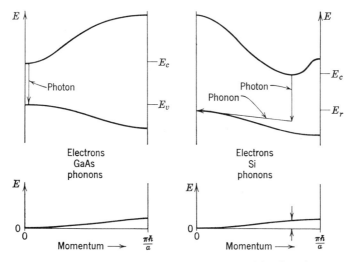

Fig. 8-5 Direct and indirect photon emission. Electron transition from lowest conduction band levels to highest valence band levels requires energy and momentum conservation. Two "particles" must interact *simultaneolusy* in Si. The same momentum and energy scales apply to both particles. Reference energy is zero for phonons (no potential energy is involved).

duction band are in states associated with $\hbar k$ near zero. The empty states in the valence band to which the transitions might proceed are, of course, the highest energy states of this band and they are also near $\hbar k = 0$. Thus electrons can drop from the conduction band to valence band with emission of the almost momentumless photons. In a reverse process, the system can absorb a photon. The energy is absorbed by one electron. Statistically, the electrons are mostly in the valence band and the empty states to which they can go are mostly in the conduction band. Transitions must be between states of nearly the same k value if no phonon is involved.

Now consider the case of silicon. An examination of Fig. 8-5 reveals that the conduction band electrons must normally be in states with $\hbar k$ near $3\pi\hbar/4a$, and the valence band holes available for them to drop into are near $\hbar k = 0$. Thus a phonon having momentum of about $3\pi\hbar/4a$ must be emitted or absorbed as the emitted photon can only account for a balance of energy. Because of the third entity, the phonon, this is known as an "indirect" transition. The phonon also has energy, though not very much. Thus for complete energy balance, for example, the photon must emit the sum of the energy difference between the two electronic states and the energy of the absorbed phonon. Transitions of this type involve "three body" collisions: the electron, the photon, and the phonon. Such occurences are rare. Thus this transition process is only very weakly involved in carrier (hole and electron) recombination. Actual processes in Ge and Si are more involved.

In the case of radiation of light quanta from atoms we have the situation where the light quanta has an ordinary momentum, though small, whereas the electronic states have angular momentum as discussed earlier. The transference between the two is shown there: the angular momentum involves ordinary momentum times a distance, the radius of the point of action. Thus the *change* in angular momentum between two states is such as to supply the ordinary momentum at the radius at which the transition is most likely. This conclusion also indicates that the direction of propagation of the emitted or absorbed light is related to the direction of the angular momentum axis of the atom.

PROBLEMS

1. (a) Show that equations (8-2), (8-3), and (8-4) follow from (8-1)
   (b) Show the derivation of equations (8-5,) (8-6), and (8-7).
2. Show that $\hat{M}^2\hat{M}_x - \hat{M}_x\hat{M}^2 = 0$.
3. The angular momentum eigenfunctions were not needed to obtain the angular momentum eigenvalues. Does it follow that sets of eigenvalues are independent of the particular system involved?
4. Maximum values of angular momentum have not been considered here. They exist and do depend on the system, but they are symmetric in the two directions (here this corresponds to positive and negative values). How, if at all, would this modify your discussion of Problem 3?
5. Work out the first-order perturbation of the energy for the lowest four levels (lowest eight states) for the perturbed potential of the figure:

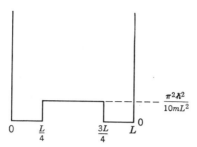

6. Work out the first-order perturbation of the energy for the lowest four levels (lowest eight states) for the perturbed potential of the figure:

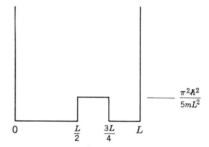

7. In Problem 5, considering only the perturbation of the lowest energy, what is the magnitude of $a_0^* a_0$? How large is the integral where subscripts zero and one here are the eigenfunctions for the lowest and second lowest energy states?

8. In the situation where a state had an eigenvalue of energy in the energy gap, the eigenfunction was attenuated rapidly as distance from the presumed impurity atom increased. Go through the equivalent formulation and determine the equivalent of equation (8-39) for an energy slightly less than the band minimum instead of greater than the band maximum as in (8-25). In (8-25) we are speaking of "acceptor" states, whereas we are now asking about "donor" states.

9. Go through the derivation for impurity states (localized state in the energy gap) for the case where the band has the form as given in Problem 7-8.

BIBLIOGRAPHY

D. Park, *Introduction to Quantum Theory*, McGraw-Hill, 1964.

W. Heitler, *Elementary Wave Mechanics with Applications to Quantum Chemistry*, Oxford University Press, London, 1956.

P. A. Lindsay, *Introduction to Quantum Mechanics for Electrical Engineers*, McGraw-Hill, 1967.

C. W. Sherwin, *Introduction to Quantum Mechanics*, Holt, Rinehart & Winston, 1959.

S. N. Levine, *Quantum Physics of Electronics*, Macmillan, 1965.

P. T. Matthews, *Introduction to Quantum Mechanics*, McGraw-Hill, 1963.

C. A. Coulson, *Valence*, Oxford University Press, 1961.

L. Brillouin, *Wave Propagation in Periodic Structures*, Dover (S-35), 1953.

INDEX